SCOPE

The purpose of this Maintenance Handbook is to act as a reference tool to help effectively manage and maintain digital relays.

This Handbook will help in the creation of an effective maintenance schedule by identifying critical components in a relay and identifying the application red flags that are detrimental to the relay's life. This Handbook will also recommend practices for maximizing the life of a digital relay, while making the most effective use of resources and time.

Included with this Handbook are specific Multilin product Maintenance Guides. They include instructions on how to perform in-service, out-of-service, and unscheduled maintenance on specific relays. Explanations and recommended actions regarding relay self-test messages are provided for fast troubleshooting. Maintenance worksheets are also included as instrumental tools to aid in performing hardware validation tests.

Written by: Vincent Thomas

For general information concerning Multilin products, please visit our website at GEDigitalEnergy.com, or contact us at:

US and Canada	1-800-547-8629	GE Digital Energy
International	905-294-6222	215 Anderson Ave
Fax	905-201-2098	Markham, Ontario, Canada
Web	GEDigitalEnergy.com	L6E 1B3

CONTENTS

MAINTENANCE PRINCIPLES

MAINTENANCE PRINCIPLES

PRODUCT MAINTENANCE GUIDES

TRAINING

QUICK TIPS

1 Introduction to Protection Relays

1.1 Technology Progression of Protection Relays

The basic objective of system protection is for the quick isolation of power system problems to minimize the impact to the rest of the system. Protection is meant to minimize the duration of faults, limit the damage of system events, and minimize the time of system outages.

The invention of the first Induction Disk relay in 1910 marked the beginning of electrical relay protection. The components of electromechanical relays are typically induction disks or cylinders turning on jewel bearings, using resistors, inductors and capacitors to define operating characteristics, and using springs and levers to define operating times. These relays involve moving parts, with movement caused by electromagnetic forces and torques proportional to the RMS values of the input signal.

Figure 1
Evolution of Protection & Control.

The 1955 introduction of the solid-state (or static) relay used electronics to mimic the characteristics of electromechanical relays. Functionality remained very similar, but certain technical and reliability issues persisted. The popularity of electromechanical relays remained strong throughout the world.

The introduction of the digital relay in 1982 signified a technological leap forward in protection. Composed of a microprocessor, analog data acquisition, relay algorithms stored in memory, contact inputs, and contact outputs, the digital relay provides greater application flexibility and is a replacement for most electromechanical relays. Having no moving parts, digital relays, unlike electromechanical relays, do not rely solely on the RMS values of the measured signal. As such, digital relays can resolve fundamental frequencies and harmonics.

Digital relays allow a variety of protection schemes to be applied with minimal additional costs and have the ability to be changed with relative ease. Continued advancements have led to the powerful multi-function and multi-processor relays of today, allowing for the inclusion of inherent diagnostic capabilities. By analyzing event records, waveforms, and trending data recorded, the digital relay not only offers protection, but aids in understanding the nature of recorded disturbances. Unlike previous technologies, digital relay self-diagnostics features provide a mechanism to monitor internal conditions and the health of the relay.

The basic criteria that protection engineers must consider when selecting methods of protecting a system are reliability, maximum continuity of service, high speed operation, simplicity, and economics.[1]

It is generally accepted that the attributes of digital relays make them the preferred choice for achieving system protection. This is proven true by looking at global sales numbers, with the vast majority of relays manufactured and purchased today being digital. The significant advantages of digital relays over electromechanical are as follows:

Advantages of Digital Relays over Electromechanical

- More protection & control for less cost
- Wiring simplification and reduction in panel space - fewer devices required
- Reduced maintenance requirements
- Diagnostic capability: event recording & waveform capture
- Ability to calculate and display distance to fault
- Built-in programmable logic for control and automation
- Self-checking / Self-testing capability
- Communication capability to design enhanced protection schemes
- Capability for remote interrogation and setting application
- Ability to change settings automatically based on system conditions

The shift from the use of electromechanical relays to digital requires changes to some previously established procedures and maintenance practices. Use of digital relay self-testing features reduces the need for certain tests, (i.e.: calibration testing), which can reduce the time requirements, expense, and frequency of full maintenance testing. The recommended tests for modern digital relays are discussed in Section 4 – Modern Maintenance Testing Methods.

1.2 Maintenance Differences Between Electromechanical & Digital Relays

In many existing facilities, the procedures for commissioning, testing, and the periodic maintenance of protection relays were created during a time when electromechanical relays were the standard protection device.

---

[1] *See Reference List on page 48.*

Whether electromechanical or digital, the objectives of testing are the same: verify AC input readings are correct, verify the relay operates properly, and verify that the protection scheme functions as designed.

The following are standard tests required for electromechanical relays, with an explanation on the differing requirements for digital relays.

Settings

Applying settings to electromechanical relays can involve adjustments to taps, levers, and/or trim pots.

Digital relay settings are loaded to the relay in electronic form via software. A commissioning test should be performed to verify that the settings have been entered correctly. Relay settings can be periodically checked as a way to identify any unauthorized setting changes.

Some digital relays have the ability to log all settings changes. These logs can be retrieved in order to trace what settings changed, when they were changed, and how they were changed.

Calibration Testing

Calibration Testing of electromechanical relays is required to ensure that the relay remains within the allowable limits for accuracy. This involves taking the relay out-of-service and connecting each discrete relay to test equipment. For any relay with readings outside allowable limits, re-calibration would be required. Calibration of electromechanical relays is typically, a very time consuming procedure requiring specialized expertise. Since environmental factors will affect operating characteristics over time, periodic calibration testing will be required throughout the life of electromechanical relays.

Periodic calibration and calibration testing is not required with digital relays to the extent that it is with electromechanical relays. Digital relay characteristics do not change with time, and internal self-tests that monitor the accuracy of calculations can detect calibration drift. In-service tests are tests performed with the relay operating and protecting the system. An in-service test to verify calibration is to compare relay values to those of another calibrated meter reading the same values. A spot check to verify relay meter readings can be done during routine walkabouts. Retrieval, analysis, and comparison of the event records from a system fault or other disturbance, against a base condition are other in-service methods for verifying calibration and relay operability.

When a digital relay is brought out-of-service in order to perform functional testing, calibration testing can be done using an injection test.

Self-Testing

With electromechanical relays, evidence of proper relay functioning is limited to the last time the relay operated, or the last time it was tested. Following an event or test, relay integrity is unknown, which is one reason why frequent periodic maintenance on electromechanical relays is recommended.

The self-testing programmed within digital relays is a way for continuous testing and monitoring of a relay. Self-testing refers to the automatic self-test diagnostic checks to ensure device integrity. Digital relay self-tests check approximately 85-90% of the hardware, perform CRC/check-sum verification on non-volatile memory, and perform background checks on processor functionality. Any failures detected are immediately communicated to the user as an alarm so that remedial action can be taken. Note that output contacts are not verified through the self-test diagnostics, and therefore must be included in a periodic test plan.

Self-tests of digital relays are more fully described in Section 4 - Modern Maintenance Testing Methods.

2 Factors Affecting Proper Operation of Relays

By identifying the critical hardware components and the major external factors that can affect the proper operation of a relay, one can best formulate the most effective maintenance plan. This section will give a summary of components commonly used by digital relay manufacturers throughout the world and describes the main factors that may cause relay misoperation and component failure. Those components that can directly affect relay protection functions should be understood to ensure they are the primary focus of relay maintenance.

2.1 Component Introduction

The lifespan of a protective relay, and indeed any electronic device, is dependent on its internal components. The failure of any single component in the relay, while not resulting in a complete failure, generally results in the relay not performing as per design.

The quality of electronic components has changed significantly over the years. The best internal components available for use in older generations of digital relays are not the best components by today's standards. As such, relay users must consider the age of a digital relay's components when assessing maintenance requirements.

2.1.1 Printed Circuit Boards (PCB)

In electronics, printed circuit boards are used to mechanically support and electrically connect electronic components to each other. The types of components connected to a PCB are resistors, capacitors, transistors, diodes, logic gates, and operation amplifiers. The conductive pathways built-in the multiple layers that make up the PCB makes the connections between these devices. PCBs are generally rugged, inexpensive, and highly reliable , while at the same time, extremely critical components.

Figure 2
Example of a Through-Hole PCB.

Figure 3
Example of a Surface Mount Technology PCB.

The two methods by which electronic components are attached to PCBs are Through-Hole (Figure 2), or Surface Mount Technology (Figure 3). An older technology, through-hole design takes the leads of components, and feeds them though holes in the board, with molten metal solder used to make the electrical connection.[2]

---

[2] *See Reference List on page 48.*

Surface Mount Technology (SMT) is the newer design, which has components soldered directly to conductive land pads on the board. The solder then acts as both the mechanical and electrical connection.[2]

This technology allows for the use of smaller components and denser board layouts, allowing for smaller products. Resistors and capacitors in particular designs have been reduced the most, with 3 to 4 surface mount resistors fitting in the space of one through-hole resistor.

Additionally, SMT yields improved shock & vibration characteristics, improved frequency response, easier shielding from Electromagnetic Interference (EMI) and Radio Frequency Interference (RFI), and easier automated manufacturing leading to greater reliability.[2]

At GE, PCBs are subject to In-Circuit Tests (ICT) to ensure that the correct components are used. This test also verifies that the components are within expected tolerances. To verify the quality of solder joints on printed circuit boards, an Automatic Optical Inspection system (AOI) has been implemented. This system automatically inspects solder joints to ensure they are within expected specifications, eliminating human visual inspection and judgment.

When PCBs are assembled into a relay, they are again tested to ensure that technical specifications are still met. An overview of the tests performed on a fully assembled relay is shown below:

Protective Relay Testing

- Visual checks
- Product code checks to ensure the as-built product matches the customer order
- Firmware code check to ensure that correct firmware is used
- Display, LED/LCD/Keypad functionality check
- Communication port functionality check
- Contact inputs check
- Exercising output contacts
- Current and voltage calibration verification
- Protection element verification
- Real-time clock check
- Voltage rails test
- Analog input and analog output verification

2.1.2 Power Supplies and Capacitors

Electronic components used in a relay require a well-regulated low voltage supply of power to function. Power supplies are critical components to the overall functionality of a relay. The power supply module in a relay is comprised of many different components, such as rectifiers, resistors and electrolytic capacitors (Figure 4).

Electrolytic capacitors, used to moderate output voltage ripple, are of particular concern when determining the lifespan of a power supply. Failure of the electrolytic capacitors will result in a power supply failure and could result in a relay failure.[3]

[2,3] *See Reference List on page 48.*

Digital relay manufacturers do not typically manufacture electrolytic capacitors. Therefore, digital relay manufacturers must select from the same group of capacitor vendors, the most appropriate capacitors to incorporate into their relay designs.

Figure 4
Example of a Power Supply board.

Electrolytic capacitors can be categorized in the following general temperature/load life grades. Note also that the rated load life of a capacitor is based on continuous usage at the maximum rated temperature. Rated load life is an industry standard measure for the guaranteed, bare-minimum, life expectancy. In actual applications, life expectancy is typically much longer than rated load life.

General-Purpose Grade Capacitors

- Used in home electronics
- -40 to 85°C temperature range
- Rated load life at max temperature: 1000 hrs or 2000 hrs

Industrial Grade Capacitors

- Used in industrial products (such as relays)
- -40 to 105°C temperature range
- Rated load life at max temperature: 1000 hrs, 2000 hrs or 5000 hrs

High Industrial Grade Capacitors

- Used in high-end industrial applications (such as relays)
- -40 to 125°C temperature range
- Rated load life at max temperature: 1000 hrs, 2000 hrs, 5000 hrs or 10000 hrs

Example: To bring these load life ratings into the perspective of use in a power supply, consider a capacitor rated for 2000 hours and 105°C. If run continuously at 105°C, the actual life expectancy is projected as 4000 hours, (½ a year). If run continuously at 25°C, the actual life expectancy is projected as 225,000 hours, (over 25 years).

The following formula is used to estimate the life expectancy of an electrolytic capacitor.

$$Lx = Lr * 2^{(To - Tx)/10} * 2^{[1 - (Ix/Io)^2]}$$

Where:

Lx = Expected Life   Lr = Rated Life at max operating conditions

To = Max rated operating temp   Tx = Actual capacitor temp

Ix = Actual ripple current   Io = Max rated ripple current

This formula, developed by capacitor manufacturers using test data, shows that the external factors that reduce the expected life of a capacitor the most, are actual capacitor running temperature and the actual ripple current. In general, capacitors with a higher maximum temperature rating will have a longer expected life.

Figure 5
Example of Capacitors.

As the technology and affordability of electrolytic capacitors continues to mature, longer life capacitors with higher temperature ratings will be available on the market for digital relay manufacturers to incorporate into their product designs.

2.1.3 Vacuum Florescent Displays (VFDs)

The display on the front of a digital relay can be used to show real-time values, user defined messages, event driven messages, and be an interface for navigating device menus for a variety of direct relay actions. Displays are typically considered non-critical components because the primary protection and control functionality of a relay is unaffected by a display failure.

The Vacuum Florescent Display (Figure 6) works using the same principles as the Cathode Ray Tubes found in traditional televisions. The construction consists of a hot cathode, an anode, and grids encased in a glass chamber under high vacuum. Changing the type of anode phosphor changes the color of the display. VFDs are an active device, meaning they produce their own light. This light is very bright with clear contrast making them easy to read.[4]

[4] *See Reference List on page 48.*

Figure 6[4]
Example of VFD technology.

The most prevalent VFD failure is a loss of brightness and clarity of the display over time. This occurrence is tied directly to the loss of chamber integrity.

The half-life of VFDs is defined as the time at which a display running continuously at 100% display power will lose 50% of its intensity. For VFDs, the rated half-life can be as low as 20,000 hours (2.3 years). Note that this half-life is not the life expectancy of the display, as 50% intensity is often perfectly suitable for use. Half-life is the display industry's standard term for accessing the useful life over time.

A VFDs lifespan is inversely proportional to the fraction of full power intensity used. In other words, lowering display power (display intensity) will extend the display life. In an effort to maximize the life of any VFDs, the display should be set to the minimum intensity required for acceptable application use.

VFDs are still available on the market today, though their overall popularity has diminished. Since 2001, GE has discontinued use of VFDs in new relays, switching to the longer lasting and more versatile technology of LCDs.

Figure 7
Example of a VFD (left) & a LCD (right) used in digital relays.

2.1.4 Liquid Crystal Displays (LCDs)

The most popular type of display used in electronic devices today is the Liquid Crystal Display or LCD. As mentioned earlier, displays are considered to be non-critical components to the core function of a relay.

Unlike VFDs, LCDs are classified as a non-emitting device, meaning they require illumination from a reflected or transmitted external light source. Utilizing two sheets of polarizing material filled with liquid crystal solution, LCDs work by applying a voltage through specific spots in the liquid. This causes light passing through the liquid crystal to be polarized one way where voltage is applied (i.e. positive), and another way (i.e. negative) where there is no voltage. When a polarizing filter is placed in front of this display, only light from one polarization passes through. This allows for the selective creation of numbers, letters, graphs, and pictures, depending on where on the screen voltage is applied.

[4] *See Reference List on page 48.*

Most LCD's use a strong light source installed behind the screen to ensure a strong contrast between the light and dark areas. Displays that use reflected light, instead of their own light source, cannot be used in low light conditions. LCDs can be monochrome or full color.[5]

LCDs are used in new product design because they are lightweight, flexible in what they can display, and use a very small amount of electric power to operate. When illuminated from a backlight source, the different types of backlights used include electro luminescent (EL), light emitting diode (LED), and cold-cathode fluorescent lamp (CCFL).

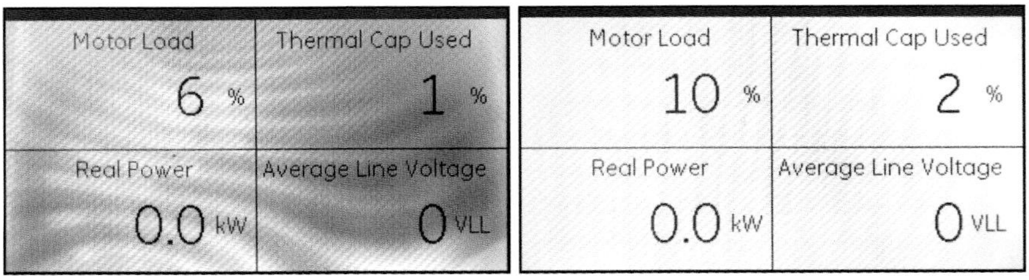

Motor Load	Thermal Cap Used		Motor Load	Thermal Cap Used
6 %	1 %		10 %	2 %
Real Power	Average Line Voltage		Real Power	Average Line Voltage
0.0 kW	0 VLL		0.0 kW	0 VLL

Figure 8
Example of LCD degradation (left) and a normal display (right).

The most prevalent LCD failure is a loss of brightness and clarity over time caused by degradation of the backlight illuminating the LCD, and the degradation of liquid crystal material.[5]

Industrial grade LCDs have backlight lamp half-life ratings (time at which the light output intensity degrades 50%), between 70,000 to 100,000 hours. Note that this half-life is not the life expectancy of the display, as 50% intensity is often perfectly suitable for use.

A half-life of 70,000 hours translates to 8 years of continuous, 24 hours per day illumination at 100% power before a 50% loss of display intensity would occur. A half-life of 100,000 hours translates to 11 years of continuous use.

As with VFDs, LCD lifespan is inversely proportional to the fraction of full power used. For this reason most LCDs are designed to require only a fraction of full display power for normal viewing.

2.1.5 Output Contacts

The ability for a protective device to function properly is dependant on two critical functions; recognition that a fault or disturbance has occurred, and the ability to signal for action when either is detected. The method for signaling action is via the device's output contacts (also known as output relays - Figure 9). Output contacts are classified as critical components to core relay functionality.

Energizing a output contact causes 'normally open' silver alloy contacts to close, while de-energizing a output contact causes the contact to open. Each time a contact opens or closes, an electric arc is produced between the silver alloy. Over time, this arcing causes wear and pitting between the two contact surfaces.

---

[5] *See Reference List on page 48.*

Figure 9
Example of a normal output contact (left) and a melted output contact (right).

Over time, the by-product of a continually operated contact is carbon and metal particle build-up. This causes additional resistance between the contact surfaces, which creates heat and increased arcing. Eventually, enough heat can be created to melt the contacts, causing the contact to fail to operate. This can be both a failure to close the circuit, or in the case of welded contacts, an inability of the contact to open when required.

Output contacts are classified as either failsafe or non-failsafe. A failsafe contact will be energized normally and is de-energized when called upon to operate. This is important for signaling a relay failure or loss of control power to the relay. A failsafe contact will be de-energized when control power is lost to the device and therefore be in its operated state.

Non-failsafe contacts are de-energized normally and are energized when called upon to operate. When control power is lost to a non-failsafe output, the output relay will be de-energized, and therefore be in its non-operated state.

Relay outputs operate in order to:

- Operate a circuit breaker to open or close/restore a circuit
- Signal an alarm condition
- Prevent re-starting of a device or process

For maintenance purposes, many digital relays have a feature that allows the state of the relay output contacts to be toggled, (opened or closed), while in test mode. Verifying the presence or absence of voltage serves as the check of relay output operation. Testing of output contacts falls outside the scope of a relay's internal self-testing. Output contacts must be tested as part of an out-of-service test procedure.

2.2 High Temperature Environments

The operating environment of a relay has a significant impact on its overall life. GE digital relays are designed to operate in the temperature range from -40°C up to +85°C. These operating temperatures are certified via testing according to IEC standards. The dry heat standard, IEC 60068-2-2, certifies proper relay operation for 16 hours at +85°C. The cold temperature standard, IEC 60068-2-1, certifies proper relay operation for 16 hours at -40°C. The environmental test, IEC60068-2-30, certifies proper relay operation in environments having up to 95% humidity, non-condensing.

Continuous operation of any relay at the extreme limits of its temperature and environmental specifications is detrimental to the long-term life of its components.

High operating temperatures are either ambient temperatures in excess of the rated operating temperatures, or heat sources that directly increase the surface temperature of the relay. High relay operating temperatures will prematurely degrade the electronic components in any electronic device unless specific precautions are taken.

Note that stress on the components in a digital relay will occur even at temperatures that are within the specified range of the device. Continuous operation at temperatures at, or close to, the maximum ratings will create more stress on the components than if operated at the ideal operating temperature of 25°C, where relay life is maximized.

> **Specific Precautions:**
>
> - Ensure the ambient temperature rating is appreciably lower than the max operating temperature.
> - Ensure relays are not located near space heaters, power transformers, or other heat producing devices.
> - Avoid mounting relays directly on top of other relays or electrical devices. Ensure airflow around the relay is maximized.
> - Check relay condition more frequently when they are located in the high temperature environments within Motor Control Centers (MCC) or adjacent to control power transformers in starters.

The power supply in digital relays are sensitive to high temperatures. Power supply failure is often attributed to electrolytic capacitor failure due to overheating.[6] This is a severe relay component failure because without the power supply, the relays will no longer function.

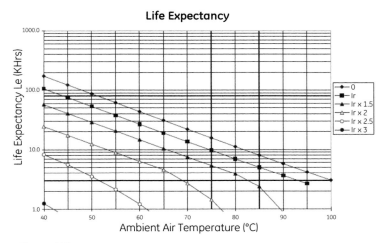

Figure 10[7]
Capacitor Life Expectancy vs Temperature and Ripple Current (Ir).

[6, 7] *See Reference List on page 48.*

Over time, capacitors lose their capacitance, a condition that is significantly accelerated when overheated.[6] As a rule of thumb, capacitor life will approximately halve with every 10°C increase in running temperature. As such, a capacitor rated for 5000 hours at 105°C will have an estimated application life of 25 years when running at 60°C, dropping to 12.5 years when running at 70°C. This is of particular concern for relays operated at high temperatures, as the actual running temperature of internal components may be as high as 20°C above the ambient temperature.

The graph (Figure 10) shows the negative effects of increasing ambient air temperature and increasing ripple current have on the life expectancy of a capacitor.

High operating temperatures can also effect the relay display. LCDs, and more specifically the liquid crystal material within the display chamber, can be permanently damaged in extreme temperatures. The result will be a loss of display resolution, discoloration, and display dead spots. (see Figure 8)

2.3 Low Temperature Environments

The low temperature rating of a relay is often limited by the rating of the LCD. GE relays conform to IEC 60068-2-1, for operation down to -40°C. While the display is not a critical component in the relay performing proper protection, the display is a method to view alarms and verify system status. The low temperature specification limits for LCDs vary by display manufacturer, with some functioning down to -30°C , while others have a limit of only -10°C.

When a LCD is brought to temperatures below its rated temperature, the crystal material can be slow, or even fail to polarize in response to changes in control signal. Visually, this will result in a LCD that will have a slow refresh rate, or will "freeze" on the last screen it displayed before the crystal became too cold to change. A return to a higher temperature can return the display to normal responsiveness. However permanent damage to the crystals can occur at below rated temperatures, which would result in permanent non-responsive patches, bubbles, and color distortion.

Additionally, energization of LCDs at low temperatures are strenuous on the backlighting (CCFL or LED). At lower temperatures, higher voltages are needed for these backlights to function. Higher voltages may result in permanent damage to the backlights, significantly lowering their overall life expectancy. This will have the overall result of a display with lower intensity and decreased resolution.

2.4 Harsh Chemical Environments[8]

Harsh Environments for digital relays include those with high humidity and condensation, high sulfur content, high ammonia content, high sulfide content, high acidity, or high particulate density. Corrosive agents with these properties, found both naturally and in certain industrial environments, are Hydrogen Sulfide gas, Chlorine, Sulfur Dioxide, and Nitrogen Dioxide.

The majority of PCB (printed circuit boards) used in digital relay manufacturing employ Surface Mounted Technology, (SMT), with copper and silver used extensively for their ideal electrical and thermal properties. Unfortunately, copper and silver are also prone to 'attack' from the corrosive gases listed above. Digital relays applied in environments with high levels of these harsh chemicals can result in corrosion damage and possible failure of surface mounted components.

[6, 8] *See Reference List on page 48.*

Figure 11
Surface Mount Resistors Showing Hydrogen Sulfide Corrosion.

Environments containing Hydrogen Sulfide are of particular concern. It is known that concentrations of as little as 10ppb of Hydrogen Sulfide may attack SMT components, and it is for this reason that it is generally the most damaging of the corrosive gases to SMT PCBs.

Corrosive Agents:
• Hydrogen Sulfide (H_2S) – corrosive effects on silver and copper
• Sulfur Dioxide (SO_2) – strong corrosive effect on nickel, steel, and zinc
• Nitrogen Dioxide (NO_2) – acts as an oxidant
• Chlorine (Cl_2) – strong synergistic effect when combined with H_2S

Long filaments of silver sulfide known as "Silver Whiskers" (Figure 12, 13) can form on the surface of silver electrical contacts of electronic SMT components, when exposed to environments containing low levels of Hydrogen Sulfide (H_2S). These formations can be further accelerated by the presence of heat and moisture. These deposits can create shorts or open circuits that can cause a relay to ultimately malfunction or fail.

Figure 12
Corrosion to internal silver material "Silver Whiskers".

Although modern digital relays are extremely robust, (meeting and exceeding ANSI/ IEEE standards for survivability in utility and heavy industrial environments), specific environmental hazards such as the effects of Hydrogen Sulfide gas and other corrosive agents on the SMT components, need to be specifically addressed.

Applying a Harsh Environment Conformal Coating to the circuit boards of protective relays is one solution that addresses this issue. Harsh Environment Conformal Coating is engineered to resist Hydrogen Sulfide gas and other corrosive agents, including humidity. This coating is a specially designed paste that covers electronic components, shielding them from coming in contact with corrosive agents.

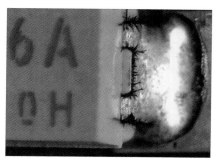

Figure 13
Corroded surface mount capacitor.

This Harsh Environmental Conformal Coating improves and extends the working life of the product and increases the reliability of performance.

Other solutions exist in dealing with corrosive chemical environments. Techniques such as air filtration and switchgear louver filters with activated carbon are sometimes used as a mitigation approach to reduce Hydrogen Sulfide in the air. In addition to being a more expensive solution to implement than conformal coating, problems occur when air filtration systems do not work properly, or are not properly maintained with frequent filter changes.[9]

The Harsh Environment Conformal Coating option is strongly recommended for all relays operating in chemically harsh or high moisture environments, including:

- Oil & Gas
- Petrochemical
- Pulp & Paper
- Waste Water
- Water Treatment Plants
- Primary Metals
- Mining
- Any facility where Hydrogen Sulfide or other corrosive gases are used in the manufacturing process
- Places where a high concentration of vehicle exhaust fumes exist

---

[9] *See Reference List on page 48.*

Harsh Environment Conformal Coating of relay printed circuit boards is available as an option on new relays, as well as an upgrade to existing relays.

GE relays already existing in the field can be upgraded with Harsh Environment Conformally Coating to their circuit boards.

The Harsh Environment Conformal Coating used by GE is approved to military specification MIL-I-46058-C, type AR, ER and UR. It is also 100% solvent free and UL recognized according to specification UL746C/94 for indoor and outdoor applications up to 120°C.

IEC standard 60068-2-60 defines the corrosive environment atmosphere and test methods. The Harsh Environment Conformal Coating solution used by GE is designed to protect in Class I, Class II, and Class III applications.

Harsh Chemical Environment Classifications

Class	Hydrogen Sulfide (parts-per-billion)	Application
I	0-10ppb	Well-controlled office environment with continuous adjustment" Least Corrosive"
II	10ppb	Industrial environment
III	100ppb	Industrial environment, including storage areas with poor environment control
IV	200ppb	Industrial environment near primary source of corrosive gas "Most Corrosive"

Class IV environments are so harsh, that conformal coating solutions alone will not properly protect the PCB. Additional techniques, such as air filtration using activated carbon or other filtering, are necessary in environments with air containing Class IV concentrations of corrosive agents.

Note that conformal coatings offered by other digital relay manufacturers do not necessarily comply with these same standards, and it should not be assumed that any PCB described as conformally coated will perform up to Class III environments. Investigation should be done with the relay manufacturer to determine the compliance levels of various conformal coating solutions.

2.5 High Electrical Stress Environments

Another environmental effect that can impact the proper operation of a digital relay is high electrical stress, including high voltage transients, high electrostatic discharge (ESD), and high levels of harmonic distortion.

Relays are type tested to certify their ability to withstand a certain amount of electrical stress, but exceeding the specified limits of the relay can lead to relay damage and/or false relay response. Check the product specifications of relays for the list of specific type tests passed.

High voltage, high frequency transients have been identified to affect proper relay operation. A transient is defined as a short-lived oscillation in an electrical system (usually of higher frequency than the power system fundamental frequency) that is caused by a sudden change in voltage, current or load. Sudden voltage changes commonly occur when a switching device is operated and during faults. For example, voltage transients may be generated through the switching of breakers and high-voltage capacitors.

Digital relays are tested according to electrical standards to qualify their resiliency to transients. Fast transients are typically tested to IEEE C37.90.1, IEC61000-4-4, and IEC60255-22-4 for voltages up to 5KV. Oscillatory transient are tested to IEEE C37.90.1 and IEC61000-4-12 at 2.5KV.

For a digital relay's ability to withstand electric stress to its rated levels, it is important that all ground connections recommended in the relay installation instructions be applied. A good ground connection has three benefits. First, proper grounding ensures the safety of the operator by providing some protection against shock. Second, it protects the device from the effects of electrostatic discharges (ESD), voltage transients, and electromagnetic interference (EMI). This is done in digital relays via filter networks and transient protection clamps between VT input and the surge ground terminal. Finally, a good ground connection reduces electromagnetic (EM) emissions from the unit. Such emissions may cause other electronic devices in its vicinity to act erroneously. Please review relay instruction manual to review the wiring instructions and proper grounding.

Inductive loads, such as contactors, can create transients that exceed the ratings of the published specifications of relays. Regardless of type, make or manufacturer, when a product is installed in an environment exhibiting characteristics above the product specification limits, the product will degrade over time, resulting in failures.

The following example (Figure 14) shows a voltage transient that occurred when the control coil of a DC contactor was interrupted.

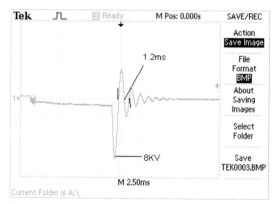

Figure 14
Harmful Voltage Transient.

This waveform shows 8KV peak voltage at approximately 800Hz frequency. The waveform exceeds the published specification level, and resulted in an unintended relay operation.

Mitigation of voltage transients can be accomplished by adding a snubber circuit across the inductive load. A snubber circuit was connected across the DC control coil of the system previously discussed. The waveform, shown in Figure 15, shows the results. Approximately 0.8KV maximum peak voltage was measured, which is multiple times less than the peak voltage of the waveform captured without the snubber-circuit. The frequency was reduced to approximately 57Hz, from 800Hz. Testing confirms that when a snubber circuit is connected across the contactor coil, the transient reduction allows the downstream digital relays to function correctly.

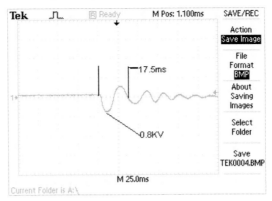

Figure 15
Suppressed Voltage Transient.

It is a common, and recommended, practice to install snubber circuits across highly inductive loads like motor contactors to reduce the generation of switching transients.

2.6 Relay Settings

For a relay to function as intended, it is important for the relay to be programmed with the appropriate settings. While this may seem like an obvious statement, the improper setting of relays is a common problem.

The person creating a setting file for a relay must have knowledge of the application that they are creating a protection scheme for. In case additional help is required, relay application engineers or consultants specializing in protective relaying should be contacted for guidance.

Once a setting file is created, one must ensure that they do not apply the setting file to the wrong relay. A way to avoid this is to use the optional "serial number lock" feature available in the setup software of some relays. By entering the serial number of the relay for which the software was intended, users prevent relay settings from accidentally being applied to the wrong relay.

The proper naming, documentation, and storing of setting files is important to ensure that the history of a device's protection is kept, for traceability of what was changed, when it was changed, and who changed it. This process is known as setting revision control. It is recommended that a process for setting revision control be established.

2.7 Relay Firmware

Firmware is the computer program embedded in relay hardware that controls the relay. Protective relay manufacturers exhaustively test all new product firmware releases prior to releasing them to customers to ensure that the products covered by the new firmware release will perform as expected. These tests include dedicated tests to verify the functionality of new features as well as regression testing to ensure that existing product functionality has not been adversely affected. Until this testing is complete, the firmware is not released to customers.

Modern microprocessor-based protective relays are complex devices that are tested to cover the extensive array of conditions the firmware is required to handle. In the event that a firmware error occurs, manufacturers work quickly to identify the cause, and make the necessary changes to correct the problem. These fixes would typically be made available as a new firmware release /revision that is field upgradeable.

The release notes accompanying a firmware release detail the criticality of the upgrade and identify features that have been added or modified. The decision to implement a firmware change should be made in accordance with the policies and practices of the facility. Contact the relay manufacturer directly with any questions before implementing a firmware change.

2.8 Security

With the proliferation of microprocessor-based protective relays that include advanced communications capabilities, one area of growing concern is the security of protection and control systems. Often when security threats are discussed, the focus is on people with intent to cause harm or interrupt processes. Overlooked are the actions of legitimate workers who have made honest mistakes during their work. The overall effect, however, could be the same interruption of a system or process.

Consideration must therefore be made to secure the integrity of a relay by establishing procedures to protect from both internal and external security threats. Multi-level passwords, security level access to equipment, and setting audit reports are possible features and security procedures that should be implemented.

2.9 In-Service Application Problems

Using a digital relay within the scope of its specified manner is crucial in assuring its proper performance, and long term operating life. For general application questions, consult the instruction manuals and other product literature. They provide specifications including the metering, setpoint, and protection ranges and accuracies. Also included are temperature ranges, communication speeds, voltage and current input ratings, and control power requirements.

For specific questions on the selection and application of digital relays, refer to the product instruction manual, product user guide, and product application notes. For Multilin devices, this information is available on the GE Digital Energy website and through use of the EnerVista™ Launchpad documentation management features. Multilin application engineers are available throughout the world to answer specific questions. Visit www.GEDigitalEnergy.com, or call 1-800-547-8629.

2.10 Summary of Actions to Prolong Relay Life

The life expectancy of electronic devices such as digital relays, are dependent on the individual components used, the circuit design of the device, and the environment in which it is applied. In general, the same components are available to all relay manufacturers. Appropriate selection of components in the relay design and proper relay applications are key in maximizing relay life. The following are application criteria that affect relay life.

Operating Temperature

- Relays will have maximum life expectancy when operated at an ambient temperature of near 25°C.
- Continuous operation at temperatures approaching the maximum temperature rating of the relay will create excess stress on components such as power supplies, capacitors, contact outputs, and displays.
- Continuous operation and start-up at temperatures approaching, the minimum temperature rating of the relay can create excess stress on displays, particularly LCDs.
- Powering up any LCD at low temperatures (below -10°C) is stressful on the liquid crystals and the CFFL backlighting, and should be avoided whenever possible.

Harsh Environment

- Relays in environments containing high concentrations of Sulfur Dioxide, Nitrogen Dioxide, and Chlorine should be treated with a conformal coating, (done by the relay manufacturer), to protect the electronic components from corrosion and silver whiskers.
- Relays in environments containing any Hydrogen Sulfide should be treated with a conformal coating, (done by the relay manufacturer), to protect the electronic components from corrosion and silver whiskers.
- Industries requiring conformal coating due to environments that are typically chemically harsh or have a high moisture continent are:
    1. Oil & Gas
    2. Petrochemical
    3. Pulp & Paper
    4. Wastewater
    5. Primary Metals
    6. Mining
    7. Any process where Hydrogen Sulfide is used.

Electrical Stress

- High voltage and high frequency transients that exceed relay specifications may affect proper relay operation.

- All ground connections recommended in the relay installation instructions should be connected. Failure to do so compromises the relay's ability to handle transients and may compromise operator safety.

- Snubber circuits should be installed across inductive loads to mitigate voltage transients.

General Maintenance

- Output contacts that are worn, pitted, or have carbon and metal particle buildup will generate more heat, leading to arcing and contact failure. Contacts should be visually checked for evidence of wearing or overheating.

- Relays with displays having adjustable power intensity , such as VFDs, should be kept at the lowest acceptable intensity to extend the display's useful life.

- LCDs typically have a longer average lifespan and have lower power requirements than VFDs. Therefore, when VFDs begin to fail, LCDs should be used as the replacement.

Products for specific protection applications are available, covering the generators, transmission, and distribution lines, as well as solutions for the protection of industrial assets such as motors and industrial processes. The criticality of the asset or process to be protected should fundamentally determine the maintenance policy and procedures required.

3 Digital Relay Maintenance Best Practices

An effective maintenance program should consist of periodic testing based on application, environment and system criticality.[10] This document outlines suggested best practices to help users determine appropriate relay maintenance programs for ensuring the integrity of the protection application. A program for the control and storage of testing history and results documentation is also highly recommended.

As discussed in Section 1 of this handbook, the differences between testing requirements for electromechanical relays and for digital relays are significant. The microprocessor-based design of digital relays includes internal diagnostic functions and self-test algorithms that make some traditional tests required for electromechanical and static relays unnecessary. The internal monitoring functionality is discussed further in Section 4.1 Digital Relay Self-Testing.

This handbook provides maintenance recommendations for digital relays manufactured by GE. These recommendations can also be generally applied to digital relays from other manufacturers. However, always defer to the relay manufacturer's product documentation for the specific procedures to follow for each relay.

3.1 Relay Audit

It is strongly encouraged that relay users perform an audit of all relays. An audit should obtain the following information from each relay:

Audit Information from the Relays
• Order code or model/part number
• Relay serial number
• Relay firmware version
• Date of commissioning
• Date of last Settings File revision
• Relay operating ambient and surface temperatures
• Note harmful environmental factors

Users can send the order code, serial number, firmware version, date of commissioning, and ambient temperature data on Multilin devices to GE Multilin Customer Service Team (CST) for complimentary evaluation and recommendations on service requirements. The GE Multilin CST will use this information to determine if any Product Advisories exist for the products, or if a general Service Bulletin exists that recommend specific action. By providing ambient and surface temperature data, evaluation can be made as to whether the relay is being applied in a suitable environment.

---

[10] *See Reference List on page 48.*

3.2 Service Bulletins and Product Advisories

Prior to performing maintenance on a relay, one should check if any recent Product Advisories or Service Bulletins exist for the relays in question. If any exist, documentation will provide the user with directions for specific maintenance actions or other recommendations.

To ensure that the most up-to-date information is accessible, contact the relay manufacturer for the most recent product documentation and for questions regarding specific relays. In the case of GE relays, one can either contact the Customer Service Department directly, or use the EnerVista™ Launchpad software to collect and organize product documentation and software.

EnerVista™ Launchpad ensures that all necessary documents, setup programs and software tools are up-to-date, by automatically retrieving updates from the GE Digital Energy website or product CD. EnerVista™ Launchpad can also be set to send the user an email whenever new information is made available.

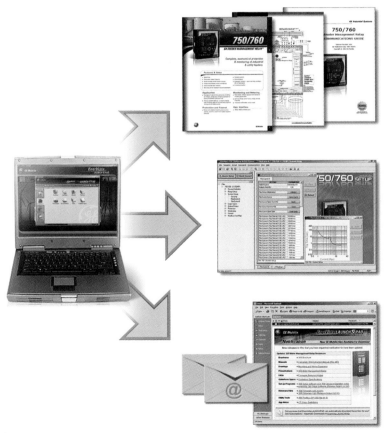

Figure 16
EnerVista™ Launchpad: Keeps critical information about GE Multilin products up-to-date.

GE Multilin Customer Service Team should be contacted for access to, or concerns regarding, historical Service Bulletins related to older relays.

Launchpad can retrieve & send email updates about:
• Production Instruction Manuals
• Application Notes
• Service Bulletins
• Guideform Specifications
• Drawings
• Support Documents
• FAQ's
• Product Brochures

3.3 Setup Software Upgrades

It is recommended that where possible, the most recent versions of the relay setup and analysis software be used. Use of the latest setup software adds greater functionality without compromising performance. While Multilin product setup software is backwards compatible (i.e. newer software versions will work with older relay), this is not necessarily the case with other relay manufacturers.

For any questions regarding the suitability of installing a new version of a relay's setup software, either read the corresponding release notes pertaining to the new software release, or contact the manufacturers technical support team.

3.4 Firmware Upgrades

Upgrading firmware, both for in-service relays, as well as in design standards, is not a trivial matter and due consideration must be given to the importance of performing these upgrades. The following recommendations and considerations should assist in making the decision on whether to upgrade relay firmware or not.

For in-service installations, it is important to identify any errors that are corrected by the upgrade to a newer firmware release.

- Any minor release of firmware is indicative of a fix to an existing firmware error. For example, for a product currently running firmware version 5.01, a firmware release 5.02 for the product would be to correct some issue with the firmware. Therefore the release notes and product service bulletins should be reviewed to determine if the noted fixes are applicable to the protection in use.

- Any major firmware release (e.g. 5.60 to 5.70 or 4.32 to 5.00) will contain new features in addition to potential error fixes and should also be reviewed for impacts to existing in-service relays.

- For both major and minor firmware releases, if there is no impact to the existing in-service protection, then there should be no immediate need to upgrade firmware.

- New features in major releases should be examined to see if there are any features that may be advantageous to have in the existing relays. An example would be the addition of advanced monitoring and equipment diagnostic elements that may provide additional information on asset health.

For design standards, the aspects to look at are similar, but the justification becomes more economic based and follows a cost/benefit analysis. For example, a new function or feature may eliminate the need to install an additional external device. The resulting cost advantage may justify the upgrade of standard designs to include the latest firmware.

Once it has been determined that a firmware upgrade is acceptable, the following steps should be followed to implement the new firmware:

- Download existing relay settings from the relay using the corresponding setup program.
- Download and save all event data, including sequence of events, oscillography and data logs using either the setup program or EnerVista™ Maintenance software.
- Notations in the relay's settings sheets or audit documentation should be made noting the previous firmware version and the new firmware version.
- Notations should also be made in the relay setting sheet if an available firmware upgrade was deferred, and the reasons for doing so. These notations act to warn other employees from unknowingly making an ill-advised change.
- Prior to uploading new settings or firmware to the relay, temporarily block relay trip functionality as an added precaution against a false trip.
- Convert setting file to the new firmware version using the corresponding relay setup software.
- Upgrade the relay firmware using the corresponding relay setup software and upload the converted setting file.
- Testing to verify proper scheme operation (functional and other).

3.5 Relay Security Recommendations

As previously discussed, compromises to the security of a protection and control system is a growing concern. Breaches to the stability of a protection and control system may be done deliberately or accidentally, either of which is unacceptable. There are methods for increasing the security of a relay and a protection system.

Beyond the standard discussions on network security (e.g. LAN firewalls, virtual private networks or VPN, secure modems), there are a number of in-the-box security tools available within modern protective relays.

Passwords:

Modern relays usually support multiple levels and types of passwords. Usually there are separate access levels provided to read relay data, make setting changes and execute controls. More advanced relays will provide separate passwords for access both through the front panel and through communications ports.

In addition to providing security against external parties that may be attempting access for malicious purposes, passwords also provide a means of preventing the inadvertent modification of, or incorrect controlling of, a relay. This is of particular importance when controls or settings uploads are being done via remote communications, where clear visual confirmation of the target relay may not be possible.

Access Switch:

Certain relays come with an Access Switch input that may be wired to a supervisory PLC/RTU contact or keyswitch. This permits a two-tier security scheme, where unless the Access Switch input is active (either keyswitch closed or PLC/RTU contact on), no settings can be modified in the relay, even if the settings password is provided. This prevents both malicious, as well as unintentional, setting changes from being made.

For greater security, it is recommended that if the Access Switch input contact is jumpered, the jumper be removed and replaced with either a keyswitch or wired to a supervisory PLC/RTU.

Settings Audit Report:

In the event of a security breach there must be a way of reconstructing events to determine what happened, and more importantly, understand how to prevent the same thing from happening again. Additionally, there may be requirements to report all security breaches internally, as well as to regulatory bodies (e.g. NERC, FDA). In order to do this, protective relays should provide a historical log of all setting change activities stored in non-volatile memory, with information regarding the nature of the changes, the date and time, and the source of the changes. The source information should include the access method (keypad, communications port), password status, and MAC address of the source computer if changes come via an Ethernet port.

Periodic examination of the setting change history will identify activities where setting changes have been made. If unauthorized changes have been made, a detailed investigation can be made to determine who made the change. Remedial actions, such as changing passwords and adding more network security, will help maximize process uptime and minimize risk of unexpected shutdowns or equipment damage.

3.6 Reporting

A secure, long-term library should be established to store relay setting files and catalog relay information such as order code, serial number, firmware version number, and commissioning date.

Setting file version control is an important reporting process that should be established to ensure a historical record exists of setting file changes. The setting file name, version number, and date of creation/modification should be recorded.

Documentation of maintenance testing results and firmware upgrades should also be reported and stored. GE Viewpoint Maintenance software is a tool that provides many of these reporting capabilities. This software permits users to download and manage event files, relay maintenance data, and setting/firmware change history.

EAST LANE 2 SECURITY/CHANGE HISTORY REPORT

Generated at: Sep 09 2005 14:30:40

Device Summary

Device Name:	East Lane 2
Device Type:	UR L90
Order Code:	L90-H03HDH-H6A-WYC
Firmware Version:	4.60
Serial Number:	MAGC0400000127
IP Address:	3. 94.247.167

Settings Summary

Setting File Name:	FAST_LINE-2.urs
Last Changed:	Sep 09 2005 14:18:03.070200 via Ethernet
Changed by Whom (MAC Address):	0008742D6FD0

Setting Changes History

Event	Date of Change	# of Changes	Password Entered	Method of Change	Changed by Whom (MAC address)	Filename Uploaded	Status	Firm. Version
144	09/09/05 02:18 PM	15	No	Ethernet	0008742D6FD0	FAST_LINE-2.urs	In Service	4.60
143	08/26/05 09:15 AM	1	No	Keypad			In Service	4.60
142	08/25/05 08:29 AM	1	No	Keypad			In Service	4.60
141	08/25/05 06:02 AM	1	No	Keypad			In Service	4.60
140	08/24/05 09:45 AM	18	No	Ethernet	00B0D0D2EA63	FAST_LINE-2.urs	In Service	4.60
139	08/09/05 05:12 AM	3	No	Ethernet	00B0D0D2EA63		Out of Service	4.60

Setting Changes Detail History

Event	Date of Change	Old Value	New Value	Item	Modbus Address
144	09/09/05 02:18 PM	Disabled	Enabled	Auxiliary UV 1 Events	0x6620
144	09/09/05 01:10 PM	Disabled	Enabled	Auxiliary UV 1 Function	0x6620
144	09/09/05 12:45 PM	Disabled	Enabled	Neutral OV 1 Events	0x6900
144	09/09/05 12:10 PM	0.300 p.u.	0.55 p.u.	Neutral OV 1 Pickup	0x6900
144	09/09/05 11:05 AM	Disabled	Enabled	Neutral OV 1 Function	0x6900
144	09/09/05 03:05 AM	Not Programmed	Programmed	Relay Programmed State	0x43E0
144	08/24/05 09:49 AM	None	F5	Source x Auxiliary VT	0x458A
144	08/24/05 03:05 AM	None	F5	Source x Phase VT	0x458A
144	08/24/05 01:12 AM	None	F1	Source x Ground CT	0x458A
144	08/23/05 11:20 PM	None	F1	Source x Phase CT	0x458A
144	08/23/05 09:10 PM	None	F5	Source x Auxiliary VT	0x4583
144	08/23/05 06:33 PM	None	F5	Source x Phase VT	0x4583
144	08/23/05 04:15 PM	None	F1	Source x Ground CT	0x4583

GE Multilin   **EnerVista VIEWPOINT** *maintenance*

Figure 17
Example of the Security Report generated by EnerVista™ Viewpoint Maintenance software.

3.7 Training

Having properly trained maintenance personnel is essential to getting the most effective use of resources and time. Familiarity with all protection features, self-diagnostic and fault-recording functions, and reporting capabilities of modern digital relays allow employees to quickly setup the relay, more quickly react to problems with the relay, and maximize the information captured by the relay.

At a minimum, new employees should be trained on the digital relays they are responsible for. Annual retraining of existing personnel is also recommended in order to refresh knowledge and keep up-to-date on new features, new technologies, and different protection philosophies.

A listing of the theoretical and product application courses offered by GE is outlined at the end of this Handbook, (GE Multilin Training Course Calendar), which includes recommendations on what type of personnel are best suited to each course. GE's Advanced Training Services offer courses to customers in the form of in-class training, on-site training, and computer-based training using interactive CDs.

3.8 Critical Asset Monitoring

GE recommends special monitoring considerations be given to assets determined to be critical. While a primary monitoring system for an entire facility likely exists for overall site monitoring, a dedicated HMI (Human Machine Interface) for critical assets, located at or near the assets in question, is recommended.

A dedicated HMI for the asset serves as an additional notification means to a centralized system. With installation in close proximity to the asset, the personnel that know the asset best, and can best react to any system event or problem, will have the information to react quickly.

EnerVista™ Viewpoint Monitoring software can act as a local HMI for this purpose. If Viewpoint Monitoring already exists in the facility as the main electrical HMI, then a Viewpoint Monitoring Viewer license can serve as the local HMI station dedicated to the critical asset.

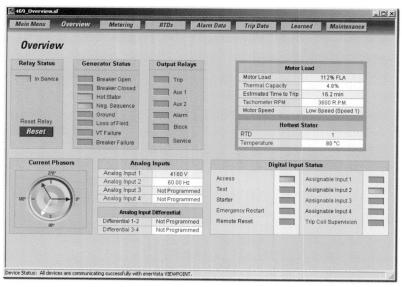

Figure 18
Sample Motor Status screen from Viewpoint Monitoring.

3.9 Relay Application Guidelines

GE relays can be used in all standard protection applications as well as in more specialized applications such as with VFD drives, synchronous motors, etc. Use of relays in non-standard or complex applications is possible provided certain factors are taken into consideration during the engineering of the system. Depending on the application, minor changes to relay set points or relay wiring may be required to achieve desired operation.

Customers are strongly encouraged to contact the GE Multilin Sales Support Application Engineering Group when questions regarding special utility and industrial applications arise.

3.10 Storehouse Spare Relays

For critical applications where the failure of a relay would result in long process downtime, or an unacceptable gap in a protection scheme, a spare replacement for that relay should be kept on hand. With the ability to quickly apply a setting file to a digital relay using setup software, a properly maintained replacement relay can be put into service very quickly.

GE recommends that spare replacement relays be powered up for a least one hour continuously at least once per year, to prevent degradation of electrolytic capacitors.

3.11 Relay Testing Precautions

When performing any type of testing on a relay that has been commissioned, every effort should be made to ensure that the relay settings and logic are not changed in any way. For example, the changing of any relay settings in order to test a function, introduces the possibility that the correct settings will not be re-introduced into the relay. As much as possible, relay testing should be done using the in-service settings of the relay.

Another common error that occurs during the testing of relays, involves simply forgetting to unshort relay current test switches. The simplicity of this error is the reason why it occurs so frequently, and why a special reminder is appropriate.

Shorting of the current test switch is required to safely remove the relay from service prior to performing tests. However, this isolates the current transformers from being read by the relay. Forgetting to remove the shorting bars before the relay is returned to service means the relay will not function properly. Relays in this situation will either leave an asset or system unprotected, or potentially false trip causing the unintended isolation of a system.

> When performing any work on electrical equipment, personnel must follow all the application safety standards appropriate to their region and their company. This includes use of all required personal protection equipment (PPE) and adhering to safe working procedures.

4 Modern Maintenance Testing Methods

The purpose of relay maintenance testing is to ensure the device is functioning properly by verifying the relay's ability to measure, detect, control and communicate properly. These maintenance criteria are covered in the self-tests, calibration tests, and functional tests detailed in this section. The advancement of digital relays, over electromechanical relays, has allowed for a new strategy for performing periodic maintenance through:[10]

- Self-test diagnostic algorithms written in firmware
- Settings inputted via software with self-checking mechanisms
- Fault recording capabilities
- Active communications including alarm condition annunciation

Note that dynamic testing has not been mentioned as a maintenance requirement. This is because dynamic testing normally involves simulating faults to verify scheme performance and element pickup, and secondary current injection to test AC inputs over their entire measurement range. While these dynamic tests are commonly performed during relay commissioning, it falls to the discretion of the user whether to perform these tests again during periodic maintenance.

The recommended testing procedures for GE relays are based on each relay's capabilities, and are outlined in the specific maintenance guide of each relay.

4.1 Digital Relay Self-Testing

The microprocessor-based design of digital relays includes analog inputs, analog to digital (A/D) converters, contact outputs, digital control inputs, and memory. Relay algorithms and settings are written to non-volatile memory meaning that the relay characteristics will not change over time. Internal monitoring of fault sensing and logic components are also written in the firmware in order to recognize and react to calibration drift, test memory and settings, and test for hardware failures. This is known as relay self-testing.

Self-tests can include, but are not limited to, monitoring of power supplies, batteries, CPUs, DSPs, A/D converters, memory, device calibration, settings mismatches, and communications failures. Through digital relay self-testing, approximately 85-90% of hardware failures can be monitored.

When an abnormal condition is detected that results in a self-test failure, a LED alert will typically activate. A descriptive message will also be displayed, and an alarm output contact may be closed (depending on the type failure). All self-test failures are automatically recorded as an event in the device event recorder. The regular retrieval and analysis of event records help verify the operability of the relay and identify potential problems or reoccurring issues.

[10] See Reference List on page 48.

The self-test relay contacts are designed to operate on critical relay failures to signal when the relay is not providing protection. In cases where relay functionality could be compromised, the relay disables trip and control functions. There is a defined list of failure modes monitored by the relay's internal self-test algorithms in the Relay Maintenance Guide section of this guide, as well as in each respective product instruction manual.

GE digital relays categorize self-test failures as either Major or Minor. Major self-test failures indicate a failure has been detected that compromises aspects of proper relay operation. Minor self-test failures indicate a problem with a relay that should be corrected, but does not compromise fundamental protection functions.

4.2 Calibration Testing/Monitoring

Relays can self-monitor and test components for calibration drifts caused by temperature and aging, and can perform a certain amount of self-correction. The scope of these capabilities will vary based on the relay type. However, it is a standard best practice to periodically verify calibration, as accurate readings are essential to relay performance.

Verification of calibration can be done by either secondary injection of AC quantities from a calibrated signal source, or comparison of the metered values with another calibrated measuring source.

4.3 Event Analysis for Functional Testing

The retrieval and analysis of event records that follow a system fault is a way to verify operability. These event reports typically include the pre-fault conditions, the fault conditions, the state of contact inputs and outputs, identification of the relay element that operated, and event waveforms. If a relay performs as intended during a fault condition, event record files of the fault can serve as documentation of passed functional test.

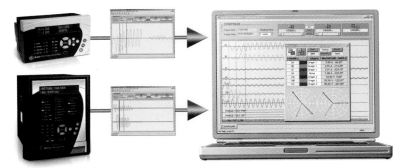

Figure 19
Retrieve and analyze event record data.

The digital relay fault data will indicate how the power system and other devices responded to the control signals of the relay. Reviewing the event report would indicate if a failure occurred with external relay connections, relay settings, contact inputs or contact outputs. Comparison of this information to another reference can serve as confirmation of relay calibration and proper operation.

4.4 Output Contact Monitoring

Output contacts are critical relay components, allowing for equipment control and alarming. Testing an output contact requires activation of the contact, and this testing should only be done if the relay is out-of-service. For this reason, no internal self-test exists. Instead, proper operation is safeguarded through contact monitoring and redundancy. If a contact fails to function as expected, an alarm condition occurs. A redundant contact may also activate to ensure the proper operation is carried out.

Example 1: The 469 motor protection relay has a Starter Failure feature that monitors the starter status contact (52a or 52b) and the motor current after the relay initiates a trip. If current is still present, or the starter contacts don't change state after a preprogrammed time delay, an alarm occurs. This alarm is programmed to a separate output contact that would then be wired to take the appropriate action (i.e. trip upstream breaker, signal control room, etc).

Example 2: The SR750 feeder protection relay has the 50BF function that can be enabled to protect against a failed circuit breaker. The operation of the 50BF function is similar to the 469's starter failure function, in that it monitors the phase current present after a trip command exists. If the current is still present after a user programmable time delay, the 50BF function operates.

Example 3: The MMII motor protection relay has a built-in welded contactor alarm that will provide the same functionality as the 469 Starter fail function. Auxiliary contacts mechanically linked to the contactor itself are used to feed back to the contactor status inputs. No status change following a "start" command indicates an open contactor control circuit and no status change following a "stop" command, indicates a welded contactor alarm.

The timely operation of contact inputs and outputs during an operate condition while in-service should be considered as a functional test 'pass'. Relay outputs can also be verified during functional testing by exercising the input and output contacts. A relay 'test mode' will often allow for the activation of output contacts when the relay is out-of-service.

> NOTE: Inadvertent tripping or activation of control schemes is to be avoided, so sufficient care must be taken to fully isolate I/O prior to exercising contacts. The blocking of relay trip functions during settings and firmware changes is an added precaution for avoiding false tripping.

4.5 Maintenance Test Summary

Use of the advanced functions in today's digital relays such as self-testing and event recording analysis, in combination with other traditional relay tests, are the recommended methods for maintaining a digital relay.

Periodic maintenance may involve in-service and out-of-service maintenance. In-service maintenance, also known as load testing, is done while the relay is in-service and carrying load quantities. Out-of-service occurs when the relay is physically isolated from the system and is no longer providing asset protection. Unscheduled maintenance can also occur when routine monitoring uncovers a relay problem.

In-service maintenance:

- Visual verification of analog value integrity such as voltage and current. Comparing metered values of the device with that of a corresponding system or device.
- Visual verification of active alarms, relay display messages, self-test alarm messages, and LED indications.
- LED test.
- Visual inspection of relay's physical condition, noting any damage, corrosion, excessive dust, loose wires, etc.
- Retrieve event record files and compare recorded data with other independently verified event information.
- Review setting file change history and compare as-is relay settings with as-left setting files. This can be done via manual comparison of each setting element, or automatically using EnerVista™ Viewpoint Maintenance software.

Out-of-service maintenance:

- Perform all in-service maintenance tests.
- Check the integrity of wiring connections.
- Analog values (currents, voltages, RTDs, analog inputs) injection test and metering accuracy verification. Calibrated test equipment is required.
- Secondary injection testing of AC quantities and DC signals.
- Contact inputs and outputs verification. This test can be conducted by direct change of state forcing or as part of the system functional testing.
- Pushbutton continuity check.

If these tests show that any element of the relay is defective, contact the relay manufacturer for recommendations. Depending on the nature of the failure, it is not always necessary to remove the relay from service.

Unscheduled maintenance:

There are several events that may result in unscheduled maintenance being required on a protective relay, including:

- Relay self-test errors or detected hardware failure.
- Unexpected protection operation for an external fault that otherwise should not have resulted in tripping.
- Failure of protection to trip for an internal fault that resulted in the operation of an upstream protection device to clear the fault.

In cases where there is a relay failure or inappropriate relay response, full out-of-service maintenance, including functional testing, may be required. The relay manufacturer should be contacted for technical support. Collect the following from the relay to submit to the relay manufacturer's customer service department.

- Serial number
- Order code
- Firmware version

- Setting file
- Event record file
- Captured waveforms file

4.6 Relay Maintenance Intervals

Philosophy

The purpose of performing periodic maintenance on any system is to maximize the probability that the system will perform its intended task when called upon to do so. More importantly, this maintenance will likely detect degradation in relay performance prior to the occurrence of a relay failure.

Relay life expectancy is a product of many factors including environment, application, and component age. All electronic devices have a life expectancy defined by the life expectancy of its individual components. Digital relay components that employ today's longer life technology, and are applied in ideal environments, can last over 20 years. However, degradation of components will occur when they are exposed to high temperatures, high electrical stresses, and/or harsh environments, reducing component life significantly.

Factors that negatively affect relay component life are discussed in Section 2. By understanding the factors that negatively affect a relay's components, one can devise the best maintenance methods and time intervals. For example, a digital relay applied in a high temperature environment should be checked much more frequently than a relay operating at 25°C ambient temperature.

At a minimum, visual checking of relay alarms and relay messages should be done during all site walkthroughs or inspections. Event records following a system event should also be evaluated. Viewing the performance of the device in reaction to a system event, and comparing the recorded values to the steady state, non-fault condition, is a means of checking measurement accuracy and relay functionality.

Though many digital relays have self-testing of individual component blocks, a schedule for periodic maintenance using supplementary testing will help detect relay problems and potential concerns.

A familiar example that shows the need for both in-service testing and periodic out-of-service maintenance, is that of a personal vehicle. An in-service check of the brakes would come from the driver noting changes in brake performance during normal use. Loss in brake performance can be noticed before complete brake failure occurs. A driver risks their safety if real-time warnings are ignored. Leaving all evaluation to be done only by a mechanic at a garage during periodic out-of-service maintenance would be irresponsible.

However, as all vehicle owners know, it is not possible to detect and identify all car problems through driving alone. Periodically taking the vehicle to a mechanic for a more thorough evaluation is valuable practice. If maintenance intervals are too long, one risks the vehicle breaking down during use. If maintenance intervals are too short, the vehicle will be out-of-service too often, and the fees paid to the mechanic will be excessive.

This is why, in addition to in-service maintenance (monitoring events, alarms and self-test messages), it is advisable that all protective relays have periodic out-of-service maintenance performed, (including functional testing). This will find problems that could impact protection performance, that would be otherwise undetected by relay self-tests.

The philosophy on how an organization determines their preventative maintenance schedule, will ideally follow one, or be a combination of, the following practices:

- **Periodic Maintenance:** Also known as Time Based Testing, periodic maintenance follows a predetermined calendar based schedule for testing relays. This method is the easiest to implement.[11]

- **Performance Based Testing:** Incorporates analysis of the relay's performance during recent events, with extension of a maintenance interval occurring when the relay has proven to perform as expected. This practice is valid only for instances where the relay in question experiences periodic fault operations. Note that proper relay operation during one event does not necessarily confirm that all relay functions are operational.[11]

- **Condition Based Testing:** Determines maintenance test intervals based on historical relay performance, the criticality of the asset being protected, and the failure mode expected by the relay, should it fail. A method for extending maintenance interval length in the interests of saving time and resources, this method requires continued analysis of a well-kept database of historical maintenance needs. Determination of a maximum allowable interval ensures maintenance is not pushed back indefinitely.[11]

The determination for maintenance interval length should include, but is not limited to, the following factors.

Factors to Consider when Selecting Maintenance Intervals
• Outage Impact: Forcing an outage on a process in order to perform routine relay maintenance may have unacceptable economic consequences. Therefore, where possible, relay testing should be coordinated with planned facility maintenance shutdowns.
• Older technology relays will have little, if any, internal-self monitoring functions. Therefore, more frequent out-of-service maintenance is required to ensure failures do not remain undetected.
• Relays having internal-self monitoring and event recording functions can extend out-of-service maintenance intervals by performing in-service maintenance and continuously monitoring and analyzing alarms and events.
• The longer a relay has been in service, the more the relay components will have experienced wear, thus increasing the likelihood of component degradation. Therefore, relay age is a factor in increasing maintenance frequency.
• For critical assets, or assets where the cost of replacement, both in terms of actual dollars and the associated downtime, are excessive, it may be desirable to perform maintenance more often.

Overall, the need for periodic out-of-service maintenance must be based on an assessment of risk of the different relay failures types, and their impact on assets and processes. Undetected failures that result in a relay tripping when no fault exists,

[11] *See Reference List on page 48.*

will interrupt processes and have an undesirable economic impact. Conversely, undetected failures that result in a failure of the protection to operate, not only result in process interruption, but also in potentially irreparable damage to key assets. The economic impact of an undetected relay failure must also be compared against the economic cost for performing periodic out-of-service relay maintenance (process outage, personnel).

Regulatory Standards & Publications

NERC (North American Electric Reliability Corporation) is a self-regulatory organization whose mission is to improve the reliability and security of the bulk power system in North America. NERC is subject to audit by the US Federal Energy Regulatory commission (FERC) and governmental authorities in Canada. NERC addresses the maintenance and testing of relays protecting bulk electrical systems in their standard PRC-005-1.[12] It states a maintenance program should include:

- Intervals for maintenance and the basis for interval determination.
- Summary of maintenance and testing procedures.
- Evidence that maintenance tests were completed in accordance to the schedule, including dates that each relay was tested.

In 2007, FERC passed Order 693 mandating the requirement of North American utilities to implement a maintenance and testing program that follows the guidelines of the NERC standards. The applicable NERC standards for digital protection relays are:

- PRC-005-1 for Transmission and Generation Protection
- PRC-008-0 for Underfrequency Load Shedding Equipment
- PRC-011-0 for UVLS System Maintenance and Testing
- PRC-017-0 for Special Protection System Maintenance and Testing

Recommendations on determining relay maintenance testing frequencies are discussed in the following documents from recognized councils and subcommittees conforming to NERC guidelines for utilities.

- WECC Relay Work Group, "Installation and Maintenance Guideline for Protective Relay Systems", March 9, 2007.[11]
- Mid Atlantic Area Council (MAAC), "Protection System Maintenance and Testing Program Audit Procedures, Document C-4", August 31, 2005.[13]
- PJM Relay Subcommittee "Relay Testing and Maintenance Practices", February 26, 2004 created to comply with NERC planning Standards III.A.M4, III.D.M5, and III.F.M6.[14]
- Northeast Power Coordinating Council (NPCC), "Maintenance Criteria for Bulk Power System Protection, Document A-4", August 30, 2004.[15]
- Northeast Power Coordinating Council (NPCC), "Guide for Maintenance of Microprocessor Based Protection Relays, Document B-23," July 14, 2004.[16]

The maintenance criteria from the NPCC, 1 of the 8 Regional Reliability Councils that work to improve the reliability of the bulk power system, is shown in Figure 20.

[11, 12, 13, 14, 15, 16] *See Reference List on page 48.*

	Electromech. Protection Group Design	Solid-State Protection Group Design	Microprocessor-Based Protection Group Design (Digital Relays)
Transmission Line Protection Groups	2 Years	2 Years	6 Years
Transformer, Bus Shunt Reactor and Capacitor Protection Groups	4 Years	4 Years	6 Years
Protection required for the NPCC Automatic Underfrequency Load Shedding Program*	2 Years	2 Years	6 Years
Generator Underfrequency Tripping Relays*	2 Years	2 Years	6 Years
All Other Protection Groups	2 Years	2 Years	6 Years

Figure 20   ** Calibration verification only*
NPCC Relay Maintenance Criteria.[15]

Additionally, PJM Interconnection, a regional transmission organization covering 13 states, recommends the following tests for communications and disturbance recording:

1. Relay Communication Channel Testing:

Unused or seldom used relay communication channels should be tested at the same frequency as that of the protection system they are associated with. Continuously monitored communications channels require maintenance only in the event of a communications failure.[14]

2. Relay Disturbance Recording Testing:

Periodic testing of the disturbance recording functions is not required. The regular retrieval and analysis of fault recorder data will verify calibration and operability. These records should be retrieved and analyzed following each recorded disturbance.[14]

Overall, providing recommendations on the most appropriate relay testing intervals to cover all relay types and applications is not possible. While bulk electricity providers have the aforementioned standards appropriate to their applications, interval decisions for all relay users should be based on:

- Type and age of the relay being used
- Type of environment in which the relays are applied
- Economics of asset/process downtime
- Economics of performing maintenance
- Criticality of the asset/process being protected
- Past history of relay failure

[14, 15] *See Reference List on page 48.*

5 Summary of Relay Maintenance Recommended Actions

5.1 Managing the Factors Affecting Proper Relay Operation

Actions Based on Environmental Factors

- Operate relays in a controlled environment to extend relay life.
- Continuous operation at, or close to, the relay operating temperature limits creates excess stress on components, reducing relay life. Actions for reducing relay temperature are:
  - Ensure free space exists between the relay and other electrical devices, allowing airflow around the relay.
  - Avoid mounting relays directly on top of, or underneath, another electrical device.
  - Provide methods for temperature control in rooms where relays are installed.
- Continuous operation and start-up at temperatures at, or close to, the minimum temperature rating of the relay will create excess stress on displays, particularly LCDs.
- Relays in environments containing high concentrations of Sulfur Dioxide, Nitrogen Dioxide, and Chlorine should be treated with a conformal coating to protect the electronic components from corrosion and silver whiskers.
- Relays in environments containing any Hydrogen Sulfide should be treated with a conformal coating to protect the electronic components from corrosion and silver whiskers.
- Industries requiring conformal coating due to chemically harsh atmospheres or having high moisture continent are:
  - Oil & Gas, Petrochemical, Chemical, Pulp & Paper, Wastewater, Primary Metals, and Mining.

Actions and Considerations for Relay Application

- Switch from electromechanical to digital relays to benefit from the increased functionality, simplified setting, self-test diagnostic capabilities and greater security.
- Ensure all ground connections to the relay are made as per the instruction manual, to increase the devices ability to handle the effects of transients.
- Install transient snubber circuits across inductive loads that create transients harmful to digital relays.
- VFDs with adjustable power intensity should be set at the lowest acceptable intensity to increase the life of the display.

- LCDs should be chosen over VFDs because LCDs typically have a longer average lifespan and have lower power requirements than VFDs.
- It is recommended to change relays' displays from VFDs to LCDs whenever this option is available.

5.2 Actions for Implementing Maintenance Best Practices.

- Perform an audit on all relays prior to performing maintenance.
  - EnerVista™ Maintenance software is a recommended tool that can retrieve device information automatically from Multilin relays.
- Submit audit data to relay manufacturers to help in getting the most recent service bulletins, product advisories and recommendations.
  - EnerVista™ Launchpad software is a recommended tool that can automatically download, organize and store the latest product advisories, service bulletins, FAQs, manuals, brochures, and applications notes.
- Upgrade to the latest relay setup program whenever possible to take advantage of the latest features and bug fixes.
  - EnerVista™ Launchpad software is a recommended tool for downloading and keeping track of all Multilin product setup programs. It will notify the user when the latest setup programs are available, and can automatically download it.
- The release notes for new firmware of any product used should be evaluated to determine if an upgrade is required.
  - EnerVista™ Launchpad software is a recommended tool that will notify the user when new firmware releases are available. Release notes and firmware can be automatically downloaded with Launchpad.
- Critical assets should have dedicated monitoring in close proximity to the asset to increase speed of maintenance response.
  - EnerVista™ Viewpoint Monitoring software is a monitoring and data recording application that provides an overview of the system, as well as collects real-time and historical disturbance data.
- A periodic maintenance schedule for in-service and out-of-service maintenance for digital relays should be established at all sites to ensure the integrity of a protection system.
- Complete out-of-service functional testing and calibration testing of digital relays should occur periodically. More frequent testing should occur if deemed appropriate by the user, based on the criticality of the asset protected, the type of relays used, the age of the relays, and the economic cost/benefit analysis that factors in costs of maintenance vs. costs of downtime and protection failure.

5.3 Maintenance Testing Method Practices

- Visually check relay alarms and relay messages during all site walkthroughs and inspections.
- Output contacts should be evaluated for wear, pitting, and carbon/ metal particle buildup, with contacts exhibiting these characteristics being replaced as a preventative maintenance action.
- Double check that shorting bars used on relay current test switches during relay maintenance are removed after maintenance testing is completed.
- Digital relay alarms should be evaluated and responded to immediately.
- Digital relay self-test error messages should be evaluated for severity (major or minor), and responded to accordingly.
- Event record files created during all detected system events should be downloaded from the relay, stored, and evaluated as soon as possible to verify proper relay operation.
- Calibration testing can be performed via secondary injection of AC quantities from a calibrated signal source.
- Comparing a relay's metered values with those of another calibrated measuring device can also serve as a means to verify calibration.

Figure 20
EnerVista™ Software tools for fast and efficient relay maintenance.

Reference List:

[1] Blackburn, J.L., Domain, T.J., 2007, "Protective Relaying Principles and Applications, Third Edition," Taylor & Friends Group, LLC, Boca Taton, Florida, pp 22-23.

[2] Web Site Free Dictionary for "Printed Circuit Boards", at: http://encyclopedia.thefreedictionary.com/printed+circuit+board

[3] Electrochemical Encyclopedia, "Electrolytic Capacitors", S. Parler, Cornell Dubilier Electronics, Inc., Liberty, South Carolina.

[4] Web Site Free Dictionary for "Vacuum Fluorescent Displays", at: http://encyclopedia.thefreedictionary.com/vacuum+fluorescent+display

[5] Web Site Free Dictionary for "Liquid Crystal Displays", at: http://encyclopedia.thefreedictionary.com/LCD

[6] Parler Jr., Sam G., "Deriving Life Multipliers for Electrolytic Capacitors," in Proc. IEEE Power Electronics Society Newsletter, vol.16, no. 1, February 2004, pp. 11-12.

[7] BHC Components Ltd., "Aluminium Electrolytic Capacitors Application Notes", November, 2002, Weymouth, Dorset, United Kingdom, pp 31.

[8] C.Cosoreanu, C.Wester, R.Midence, "Considerations When Applying Microprocessor Relays in Chemically Harsh Environments," in Proc., 60th Annual Conference for Protective Relay Engineers, March 26-28, 2007, College Station, Texas.

[9] Muller, Christopher O., "Control of Corrosive Gases to Avoid Electrical Equipment Failure," in Proc., PITA Annual Conference/PAPEX '99.

[10] Gill, Paul, "Electrical Power Equipment Maintenance and Testing," NetLibrary Incorporated, 1998, pp. 1-4, 314-337.

[11] Western Electricity Coordinating Council (WECC) Relay Work Group, "Installation and Maintenance Guideline for Protective Relay Systems", March 9, 2007.

[12] North American Electrical Reliability Council (NERC), Reliability Standard PRC-005-1: Transmission Protection Maintenance and Testing.

[13] Mid Atlantic Area Council (MAAC), "Protection System Maintenance and Testing Program Audit Procedures, Document C-4", August 31, 2005.

[14] PJM Relay Subcommittee "Relay Testing and Maintenance Practices", February 26, 2004), created to comply with NERC planning Standards III.A.M4, III.D.M5, and III.F.M6.

[15] Northeast Power Coordinating Council (NPCC), "Maintenance Criteria for Bulk Power System Protection, Document A-4", August 30, 2004.

[16] Northeast Power Coordinating Council (NPCC), "Guide for Maintenance of Microprocessor Based Protection Relays, Document B-23," July 14, 2004.

Multilin UR Family

Maintenance Guide

UR Maintenance Guide

The UR family is a series of protection, control and automation products featuring universal, modular hardware and software. This streamlines the testing process by allowing the same testing procedures to be used on all members of the UR family, including:

B30 – Bus Differential Relay

C30 – Controller

C60 – Breaker Management Relay

C70 – Capacitor Bank Protection & Control System

D30 – Line Distance Relay

D60 – Line Distance Relay

F35 – Multiple Feeder Management Relay

F60 – Feeder Management Relay

G30 – Generator Protection System

G60 – Generator Protection System

L60 – Line Phase Comparison Relay

L90 – Line Current Differential Relay

M60 – Motor Protection System

N60 – Network Stability & Synchrophasor Measurement System

T35 – Transformer Management Relay

T60 – Transformer Management Relay

URC – Universal Recloser Control

The modular hardware means that tests are only required that exercise the specific hardware within a given configuration. For example:

Example #1: C30 Controller

Order Code: C30-N03-HLH-F6D-H67-M4L

This C30 hardware configuration has 16 digital inputs, 8 Form-A outputs and 14 latching outputs. There are no modules with RTD or DCmA inputs, and the C30 does not support AC input modules. Therefore, only the Contact I/O tests needs to be performed.

Example #2: T60 Transformer Management Relay

Order Code: T60-K11-HLH-F8N-H6N-M8L-P5C

This T60 hardware configuration has 8 digital inputs, 4 Form-A outputs, 3 three-phase current input banks, 1 three-phase voltage input bank and 8 RTD inputs. Therefore, the Contact I/O tests, AC metering tests and RTD tests need to be performed.

Prior to maintenance on a relay, one should check if any service bulletins or product advisories exist for the relays in questions. This information can be found on the GE Multilin website or automatically downloaded from the EnerVista™ Launchpad document library.

If service bulletins or product advisories exist, the recommended remedial action should be implemented. Contact GE Multilin if any questions exist.

www.GEMultilin.com. 1-800-547-8629.

Recommended Tests

In-service maintenance:

1. Visual verification of analog value integrity such as voltage and current. Comparing metered values of the device with that of a corresponding system or device.
2. Visual verification of active alarms, relay display messages, self-test alarm messages, and LED indications.
3. LED test.
4. Visual inspection on relay physical condition, noting any damage, corrosion, excessive dust, or loose wires.
5. Event recorder file download with further events analysis to compare and verify recorded data corresponds with other independently verified event information.
6. Download relay settings file and check against the settings on record.

Out-of-service maintenance:

Prior to taking the relay out-of-service, it is recommended to perform the following In-service test:

1. Visual verification of active alarms, relay display messages, self-test alarm messages, and LED indications.
2. Visual inspection on relay physical condition, noting any damage, corrosion, excessive dust, or loose wires.
3. Event recorder file download with further events analysis to compare and verify recorded data corresponds with other independently verified event information.

For the following tests, the relay should be taken out-of-service.

1. Physically check wiring connections for firmness and impact relay guide clips, shorting clips for wear and damage
2. Analog values injection test (currents, voltages, RTDs, analog inputs) and metering accuracy verification. Tests the following hardware: CT inputs, ground inputs, low pass filters, sample and hold buffers, zero-crossing circuitry and multiplexer. Calibrated test equipment is required.
3. Test each relay communication port using the UR Setup program and verify functionality of RS232, RS485, and if applicable Ethernet transceivers.
4. Setting change history using Viewpoint Maintenance software, noting any unexpected changes.
5. As-is settings comparison with as-left setting files using the UR Setup software.
6. Secondary injection testing of AC quantities, DC signals to verify correct measurements are displayed.

7. Contact inputs and outputs verification. This test can be conducted by direct change of state forcing or as part of the system functional testing. Test Trip/Close coil monitors, logic inputs, solid-state outputs, output relays, analog outputs, and D/A converter.

8. Event recorder file download with further events analysis to compare and verify recorded data corresponds with other independently verified event information.

9. LED Test and pushbutton continuity check.

10. 20 second control power removal to test Super-cap / battery backup by verifying relay date and time match before and after loss of power.

If these routine tests show that any element of the relay is defective, we recommend that GE Multilin be contacted to discuss the issue and make recommendations. Depending on the nature of the failure, it is not always necessary to remove the relay from service.

Unscheduled maintenance:

There are several events that may result in unscheduled maintenance being required on a protective relay, including:

- Relay self-test errors or spontaneous hardware failure
- Unexpected protection operation for an external fault that otherwise should not have resulted in tripping
- Failure of protection to trip for an internal fault that resulted in the operation of an upstream protection to clear the fault

In all cases where there is a relay failure or inappropriate relay response, GE Multilin CST (Customer Service Team) should be contacted for technical support, including relay repair and detailed event analysis.

Self-Test Message Evaluation

Routine maintenance on the UR should begin with an evaluation of the Diagnostic Messages of the relay either through the front panel, or remotely through the EnerVista™ software program. UR relays perform self-test diagnostics at initialization  and continuously as a background task. This ensures every testable component of the hardware and software is functioning correctly. There are two types of warnings displayed when the self-test detects a problem:

Major Problem: a serious problem that compromises all aspects of relay operation.

Minor Problem: a problem with the relay that does not compromise protection.

Diagnostic messages are automatically displayed for any active conditions in the relay such as trips, alarms, or asserted logic inputs. These messages provide a summary of the present state of the relay. The Trouble LED Indicator will turn on and target message is displayed.

Self Test Message	Component / Function Affected	Severity	Failure Description
MODULE FAILURE: Contact Factory (xxx)	DSP Error, CPU Error EEPROM Data or Memory Error, and/or Failed Communication to Specified Module	Major	Module hardware failure detected. Contact the factory and supply the failure code noted in the display. The (xxx) text identifies which of the UR modules has failed (for example F8L).
INCOMPATIBLE H/W:Contact Factory (xxx)	Hardware Module(s)	Major	One or more installed hardware modules is not compatible with the relay order code. Contact the factory and supply the failure code noted in the display. The (xxx) text identifies which of the UR modules has failed.
EQUIPMENT MISMATCH:with 2nd line detail	Hardware Module(s)	Major	Hardware module configuration does not match the relay order code. Check module against the order code, ensure proper module installation, and cycle control power. Contact factory if problem persists.
MAINTENANCE ALERT:Replace Battery	Battery in Power Supply Module	Minor	The battery located in the power supply module (1H or 1L) is not functioning and needs to be replaced.
MAINTENANCE ALERT:Direct I/O Ring Break	Wiring/Connection of Inputs & Outputs	Minor	The direct input and outputs configured for a ring, but the connection is not a ring. Check direct input and output configuration and wiring.
MAINTENANCE ALERT:**Bad IRIG-B Signal**	IRIG-B Receiver and Wiring	Minor	A bad IRIG-B input signal has been detected. The cause could be a poor connection, improper cabling, malfunctioning IRIG-B receiver, or a low input signal level.
MAINTENANCE ALERT:Port ## Failure	Ethernet Port	Minor	An Ethernet connection has failed on either the primary port (Port 1) or the secondary port (Port 2).
MAINTENANCE ALERT:SNTP Failure	Time Synchronization	Minor	The SNTP server is not responding requiring a check of SNTP configuration and network connections
MAINTENANCE ALERT:4L Discrepancy	Output Contact Latching of 4L Module	Minor	A discrepancy has been detected between the actual and desired state of a latching contact output of an installed type 4L module. Verify the state of the output contact and contact the factory if the problem persists.
MAINTENANCE ALERT:GGIO Ind xxx oscill	GOOSE Data Set	Minor	A data item in a configurable GOOSE data set is oscillating. The "xxx" text denotes the data item that has been detected as oscillating. Evaluate all logic pertaining to this item.
DIRECT I/O FAILURE:COMM Path Incomplete	Direct I/O Devices	Minor	A direct device is configured but not connected. Check direct input and output configuration and wiring.
REMOTE DEVICE FAIL:COMM Path Incomplete	GOOSE Devices	Minor	One or more GOOSE devices are not responding. GOOSE setup must be checked.
UNEXPECTED RESTART:Press "RESET" key	Module or DC Supply	Minor	Abnormal restart from modules being removed or inserted while the relay is powered-up, when there is abnormal DC supply, or as a result of internal relay failure. Contact the factory.

UR Maintenance Worksheet

Hardware Functional Tests

Device Summary	
Device Name:	
Device Type:	
Order Code:	
Firmware Version:	
Serial Number:	
IP Address:	
Modbus Slave Address:	

Settings Summary	
Setting File Name:	
Last Changed:	
Changed by Whom (MAC Address)	

> Do not change relay setting in order to perform maintenance testing on relays that have been commissioned.
>
> Download the relay settings file and have these values available to conduct the following functional tests.

Source Current Accuracy Test

The UR specification for accuracy of the AC current inputs is ±0.25% of reading or 0.1% of rating (whichever is greater) from 0.1x to 2.0x nominal.

The UR AC inputs are arranged in three-phase banks, each with four AC input channels. In the case of a current input (or CT) bank there are channels for phases A, B, C as well as ground (G).

Within the UR, the AC inputs are assigned to a logical grouping known as a Source, which is then used by the various protection and control elements within the relay. Each Source may contain voltages (phase and/or auxiliary) and currents (phase and/or ground), and the currents assigned to a given Source may be either a single CT bank or a summation of several CT banks.

To test the accuracy of the AC current inputs:

1. Determine the Phase and Ground CT Primary and Secondary values from Settings > System Setup > AC Inputs > Current Bank F1.

2. Determine which Sources make use of the given CT bank from Settings > System Setup > AC Inputs > Signal Sources.

3. With secondary measurement circuits safely isolated, inject AC current into the CT bank inputs as per the corresponding table below.

4. Read the corresponding Source metering values to verify accuracy of the measured values.

View the corresponding measured values in:

Actual Values > Metering > Source 1(2) > Phase Current SRC 1(2)

Actual Values > Metering > Source 1(2) > Ground Current SRC 1(2)

5 A Secondary

					AC Sources		
			Source:				
			Name:				
Phase Current Input			Phase CT:				
CT Bank	CT Primary	CT Secondary	Injected Current	Expected Reading	Actual Reading		
					A	B	C
		5 A	0.5 A				
			1 A				
			2.5 A				
			5 A				
			7.5 A				
			10 A				

			AC Sources		
			Source:		
			Name:		
Ground Current Input			**Ground CT:**		
CT Bank	**CT Primary**	**CT Secondary**	**Injected Current**	**Expected Reading**	**Actual Reading**
			0.5 A		
			1 A		
		5 A	2.5 A		
			5 A		
			7.5 A		
			10 A		

1 A Secondary

			AC Sources				
			Source:				
			Name:				
Phase Current Input			**Phase CT:**				
CT Bank	**CT Primary**	**CT Secondary**	**Injected Current**	**Expected Reading**	**Actual Reading**		
					A	**B**	**C**
			0.1 A				
			0.5 A				
		1 A	0.5 A				
			1 A				
			1.5 A				
			2 A				

				AC Sources		
			Source:			
			Name:			
Ground Current Input			Ground CT:			
CT Bank	CT Primary	CT Secondary	Injected Current	Expected Reading		Actual Reading
			0.1 A			
			0.5 A			
			0.5 A			
		1 A	1 A			
			1.5 A			
			2 A			

Repeat the above tests for each configured Source and corresponding CT bank(s).

Source Voltage Accuracy Test

The UR specifications for accuracy of the AC voltage inputs is +/-0.5% of reading from 10V – 208V.

The UR AC inputs are arranged in three phase banks, each with four AC input channels. For voltage (or VT) banks, the channels are phases A, B, C and an auxiliary voltage input (X).

To test the accuracy of the AC voltage inputs (if available):

1. Determine the Phase and Auxiliary VT Connection, Nominal Secondary and VT Ratio values from Settings > System Setup > AC Inputs > Voltage Bank F5.
2. Determine which Sources make use of the given VT bank from Settings > System Setup > AC Inputs > Signal Sources.
3. With secondary measurement circuits safely isolated, apply AC voltage into the VT bank inputs as per the corresponding table below.
4. Read the corresponding Source metering values to verify accuracy of the measured values.

View the corresponding measured values in:

Actual Values > Metering > Source 1(2) > Phase Voltage SRC 1(2)

	AC Sources				
Source:					
Name:					
Phase VT:					

Phase Voltage Input						**Actual Reading**		
VT Bank	**VT Connection**	**VT Ratio**	**VT Nom. Secondary**	**Applied Voltage**	**Expected Reading**	**A**	**B**	**C**
				25%				
				50%				
				100%				
				125%				

Actual Values > Metering > Source 1(2) > Auxiliary Voltage SRC 1(2)

	AC Sources			
Source:				
Name:				
Auxiliary VT:				

Auxiliary Voltage Input						
VT Bank	**VT Connection**	**VT Ratio**	**VT Nom. Secondary**	**Applied Voltage**	**Expected Reading**	**Actual Reading**
				25%		
				50%		
				100%		
				125%		

Repeat the above tests for each configured VT bank(s).

RTD Accuracy Test

The UR specification for RTD input accuracy is +/- 2°C. Beginning with RTD Input 1, perform the following steps.

1. Determine the RTD Type from Settings > Transducer I/O > RTD Inputs
2. Apply resistances to the RTD input as per the table following the worksheets to simulate the RTD and verify accuracy of the measured values.

View the measured values in:

Actual Values > Metering > Transducer I/O > RTD Inputs > RTD Input xx

Repeat these steps for the remaining RTDs.

Transducer Module:						
RTD Input 1			**RTD Input 2**			
RTD ID:			RTD ID:			
RTD Type:			RTD Type:			
Expected RTD Temperature Reading (° Celsius)	Applied Resistance	Measured RTD Temperature	Expected RTD Temperature Reading (° Celsius)	Applied Resistance	Measured RTD Temperature	
-50			-50			
0			0			
50			50			
100			100			
150			150			
200			200			
250			250			

Transducer Module:					
RTD Input 3			RTD Input 4		
RTD ID:			RTD ID:		
RTD Type:			RTD Type:		
Expected RTD Temperature Reading (° Celsius)	Applied Resistance	Measured RTD Temperature	Expected RTD Temperature Reading (° Celsius)	Applied Resistance	Measured RTD Temperature
-50			-50		
0			0		
50			50		
100			100		
150			150		
200			200		
250			250		

Transducer Module:					
RTD Input 5			RTD Input 6		
RTD ID:			RTD ID:		
RTD Type:			RTD Type:		
Expected RTD Temperature Reading (° Celsius)	Applied Resistance	Measured RTD Temperature	Expected RTD Temperature Reading (° Celsius)	Applied Resistance	Measured RTD Temperature
-50			-50		
0			0		
50			50		
100			100		
150			150		
200			200		
250			250		

Transducer Module:					
RTD Input 7			**RTD Input 8**		
RTD ID:			RTD ID:		
RTD Type:			RTD Type:		
Expected RTD Temperature Reading (° Celsius)	Applied Resistance	Measured RTD Temperature	Expected RTD Temperature Reading (° Celsius)	Applied Resistance	Measured RTD Temperature
-50			-50		
0			0		
50			50		
100			100		
150			150		
200			200		
250			250		

RTD Resistance-Temperature Reference

Expected Temp. (° Celsius)	RTD Type			
	100 Ω Platinum (Ω)	120 Ω Nickel (Ω)	100 Ω Nickel (Ω)	10 Ω Copper (Ω)
-50	80.31	86.17	71.81	7.1
0	100	120	100	9.04
50	119.39	157.74	131.45	10.97
100	138.5	200.64	167.2	12.9
150	157.32	248.95	207.45	14.83
200	175.84	303.46	252.88	16.78
250	194.08	366.53	305.44	18.73

Digital Inputs

The UR Digital Inputs (contact inputs) can be verified easily with a simple switch or pushbutton. Verify the DC wetting voltage with a voltmeter. Perform the steps below to verify functionality of the contact inputs. Ensure the relay is isolated from the system when performing these tests.

The status of the contact inputs can be viewed in:

Actual Values > Status > Contact Inputs

To test Contact Inputs, follow these steps:

1. Open isolating switches for all of the contact inputs. Verify that all of the contact inputs are off.

2. For each contact input, apply positive voltage from the DC wetting supply to the input. Verify that only the input under test turns on (i.e. no other contact inputs should be on).

3. Remove positive from the contact input. Verify that the input under test turns off again.

4. Repeat for the remaining contact inputs.

Contact I/O Module:____			Contact Input Status															
Contact Input	Contact I/P ID	Switch Status	1	2	3	4	5	6	7	8	9	10	11	12	13	14	15	16
1		Open																
		Close																
2		Open																
		Close																
3		Open																
		Close																
4		Open																
		Close																
5		Open																
		Close																
6		Open																
		Close																
7		Open																
		Close																
8		Open																
		Close																
9		Open																
		Close																
10		Open																
		Close																
11		Open																
		Close																
12		Open																
		Close																
13		Open																
		Close																
14		Open																
		Close																
15		Open																
		Close																
16		Open																
		Close																

Analog Inputs and Outputs (DCMA Accuracy Test)

The UR specification for DCMA (DC milliamp) input accuracy is +/- 0.2% of full scale. Beginning with DCMA Input 1, perform the following steps.

1. Determine the DCMA Range, Min. Value, Max. Value and Units from Settings > Transducer I/O > DCMA Inputs

2. Inject DC milliamps into the DCMA input as per the corresponding table below to simulate the transducer and verify accuracy of the measured values.

View the measured values in:

Actual Values > Metering > Transducer I/O > DCMA Inputs > DCMA Input xx

Repeat these steps for the remaining DCMA inputs.

Transducer Module:							
DCMA Input 1				DCMA Input 2			
DCMA ID:				DCMA ID:			
DCMA Range:				DCMA Range:			
DCMA Min. Value:				DCMA Min. Value:			
DCMA Max. Value:				DCMA Max. Value:			
DCMA Units:				DCMA Units:			
Percent of Full Scale	Injected Milliamps	Expected DCMA Value	Measured DCMA Value	Percent of Full Scale	Injected Milliamps	Expected DCMA Value	Measured DCMA Value
-50%				-50%			
0%				0%			
50%				50%			
100%				100%			
150%				150%			
200%				200%			
250%				250%			

Transducer Module:							
DCMA Input 3				DCMA Input 4			
DCMA ID:				DCMA ID:			
DCMA Range:				DCMA Range:			
DCMA Min. Value:				DCMA Min. Value:			
DCMA Max. Value:				DCMA Max. Value:			
DCMA Units:				DCMA Units:			
Percent of Full Scale	Injected Milliamps	Expected DCMA Value	Measured DCMA Value	Percent of Full Scale	Injected Milliamps	Expected DCMA Value	Measured DCMA Value
-50%				-50%			
0%				0%			
50%				50%			
100%				100%			
150%				150%			
200%				200%			
250%				250%			

Transducer Module:							
DCMA Input 5				DCMA Input 6			
DCMA ID:				DCMA ID:			
DCMA Range:				DCMA Range:			
DCMA Min. Value:				DCMA Min. Value:			
DCMA Max. Value:				DCMA Max. Value:			
DCMA Units:				DCMA Units:			
Percent of Full Scale	Injected Milliamps	Expected DCMA Value	Measured DCMA Value	Percent of Full Scale	Injected Milliamps	Expected DCMA Value	Measured DCMA Value
-50%				-50%			
0%				0%			
50%				50%			
100%				100%			
150%				150%			
200%				200%			
250%				250%			

Transducer Module:							
DCMA Input 7				DCMA Input 8			
DCMA ID:				DCMA ID:			
DCMA Range:				DCMA Range:			
DCMA Min. Value:				DCMA Min. Value:			
DCMA Max. Value:				DCMA Max. Value:			
DCMA Units:				DCMA Units:			
Percent of Full Scale	Injected Milliamps	Expected DCMA Value	Measured DCMA Value	Percent of Full Scale	Injected Milliamps	Expected DCMA Value	Measured DCMA Value
-50%				-50%			
0%				0%			
50%				50%			
100%				100%			
150%				150%			
200%				200%			
250%				250%			

Output Relays (Contact Outputs)

The UR contact outputs can be verified using the output forcing capabilities of the UR Test Mode. Perform the steps below to verify functionality of the contact outputs. Ensure the relay is isolated from the system when performing these tests.

The status of the contact outputs can be viewed in:

Actual Values > Status > Contact Outputs

1. Open isolating switches for all of the contact outputs.
2. Enable Test Mode and assert the Test Mode Initiate operand found under:

Settings > Testing

3. Each contact output can be manually forced on and off under:

Settings > Testing > Force Contact Outputs

4. Force the output on by setting to 'Energized' and verify that only the forced contact output is asserted. Where possible, the presence of DC voltage on the output circuit should be checked and only present for the given output.
5. Force the output on by setting to 'De-energized' and verify that the forced contact output drops out and DC voltage is no longer present on the output circuit.
6. Repeat for the remaining contact outputs.

Contact I/O Module:		Contact Output Status			
Contact Output	Contact Output ID	Test Condition	Actual Status	Test Condition	Actual Status
1		Energized		De-energized	
2		Energized		De-energized	
3		Energized		De-energized	
4		Energized		De-energized	
5		Energized		De-energized	
6		Energized		De-energized	
7		Energized		De-energized	
8		Energized		De-energized	

Multilin 750/760
Feeder Protection

Maintenance Guide

750/760 Maintenance Guide

Prior to maintenance on a relay, one should check if any service bulletins or product advisories exist for the relays in questions. This information can be found on the GE Multilin website or automatically downloaded from the EnerVista™ Launchpad document library.

If service bulletins or product advisories exist, the recommended remedial action should be implemented. Contact GE Multilin if any questions exist.

www.GEMultilin.com. 1-800-547-8629.

Recommended Tests

In-service maintenance:

1. Visual verification of analog value integrity such as voltage and current. Comparing metered values of the device with that of a corresponding system or device.
2. Visual verification of active alarms, relay display messages, self-test alarm messages, and LED indications.
3. LED test.
4. Visual inspection on relay physical condition, noting any damage, corrosion, excessive dust, or loose wires.
5. Event recorder file download with further events analysis to compare and verify recorded data corresponds with other independently verified event information.
6. Download relay settings file and check against the settings on record.

Out-of-service maintenance:

Prior to taking the relay out-of-service, it is recommended to perform the following In-service test:

1. Visual verification of active alarms, relay display messages, self-test alarm messages, and LED indications.
2. Visual inspection on relay physical condition, noting any damage, corrosion, excessive dust, or loose wires.
3. Event recorder file download with further events analysis to compare and verify recorded data corresponds with other independently verified event information.

For the following tests, the relay should be taken out-of-service.

1. Physically check wiring connections for integrity and inspect relay guide clips, shorting clips for wear and damage.
2. Analog values injection test   (currents, voltages, RTDs, analog inputs) and metering accuracy verification. Tests the following hardware: CT inputs, ground inputs, low pass filters, sample and hold buffers, zero-crossing circuitry and multiplexer. Calibrated test equipment is required.
3. Test each relay communication port using the 750/760 Setup program and verify functionality of RS232, RS485, and if applicable Ethernet transceivers.

4. Setting change history using Viewpoint Maintenance software.

5. As-is settings comparison with as-left setting files using the 750/760 Setup software.

6. Secondary injection testing of AC quantities, DC signals to verify correct measurements are displayed.

7. Contact inputs and outputs verification. This test can be conducted by direct change of state forcing or as part of the system functional testing. Test Trip/Close coil monitors, logic inputs, solid-state outputs, output relays, analog outputs, and D/A converter.

8. LED Test and pushbutton continuity check.

9. Keypad test to verify that each key responds to key press.

10. 20 second control power removal to test Super-cap / battery backup by verifying relay date and time match before and after loss of power.

If these routine tests show that any element of the relay is defective, we recommend that GE Multilin be contacted to discuss the issue and make recommendations. Depending on the nature of the failure, it is not always necessary to remove the relay from service.

Unscheduled maintenance:

There are several events that may result in unscheduled maintenance being required on a protective relay, including:

*   Relay self-test errors or spontaneous hardware failure.

*   Unexpected protection operation for an external fault that otherwise should not have resulted in tripping.

*   Failure of protection to trip for an internal fault that resulted in the operation of an upstream protection to clear the fault.

In all cases where there is a relay failure or inappropriate relay response, GE Multilin CST (Customer Service Team) should be contacted for technical support, including relay repair and detailed event analysis.

Self-Test Message Evaluation

Routine maintenance on the 750/760 should begin with an evaluation of any Diagnostic Messages of the relay either through the front panel, or remotely through the EnerVista™ Software program. The 750/760 relays perform self-test diagnostics at initialization and continuously as a background task. This ensures every testable component of the hardware and software is functioning correctly. There are two types of warnings displayed when the self-test detects a problem:

Major Problem: a serious problem that compromises all aspects of relay operation.

Minor Problem: a problem with the relay that does not compromise protection.

Diagnostic messages are automatically displayed for any active conditions in the relay such as trips, alarms, or asserted logic inputs. These messages provide a summary of the present state of the relay. The Message LED flashes when there are diagnostic messages present.

Self Test Message	Severity	Failure Description
A/D Virtual Ground	Major	Caused by a failure of the analog to digital converter. The integrity of the systems essential input measurements are affected by this failure.
EEPROM Corrupt	Major	Corrupted location(s) in the relay data memory has been detected, which cannot be self-corrected. Relay function is at risk of malfunctioning due to his memory error.
FLASH corrupt	Major	Caused by detection of a corrupted location the program memory. Relay function is at risk of malfunctioning due to this memory error.
Analog Output +32V	Minor	Caused by the loss of the +32 V DC power supply used to power analog outputs. Analog output currents are affected by this failure.
Clock Not Set	Minor	Occurs if the internal clock has not been set.
Dry Contact +32V	Minor	Caused by the loss of the +32 V DC power supply used to power dry contacts of logic inputs. Logic inputs using internal power are affected by this failure.
Force Analog Out	Minor	Occurs when the FORCE A/O FUNCTION setpoint is "Enabled".
Force Relays	Minor	Occurs when the FORCE OUTPUTS RELAYS FUNCTION setpoint is "Enabled".
Internal RS485	Minor	Caused by a failure of the internal RS485 communication link. Attempts to read actual values or write setpoints will produce unpredictable results.
Internal Temp	Minor	Caused by the detection of unacceptably low (less than –40°C) or high (greater than +85°C) temperatures detected inside the unit.
IRIG-B Failure	Minor	Caused when IRIG-B time synchronization has been enabled but the signal cannot be encoded.
Pickup Test	Minor	Occurs when the PICKUP TEST FUNCTION setpoint is "Enabled".
Relay Not Ready	Minor	Occurs when the 750/760 OPERATION setpoint not been set to "Ready".
RTC Crystal	Minor	Caused by a failure of the Real Time Clock circuit. The ability of the relay to maintain the current date and time is lost.
Simulation Mode	Minor	Occurs when the simulation feature of the relay is active.

750/760 Maintenance Worksheet

Hardware Functional Tests

Device Summary	
Device Name:	
Device Type:	
Order Code:	
Firmware Version:	
Serial Number:	
IP Address:	
Modbus Slave Address:	

Settings Summary	
Setting File Name:	
Last Changed:	
Changed by Whom (MAC Address)	

Do not change relay setting in order to perform maintenance testing on relays that have been commissioned.

Download the relay settings file and have these values available to conduct the following functional tests.

Phase Current Accuracy Test

The 750/760 specification for phase current accuracy is +/- 0.5% of 2 x CT when the injected current is less than 2 x CT. Perform the steps below to verify accuracy.

1. Determine the Phase CT Primary amperage from the relay settings file.
2. Inject the values shown in the table below and verify accuracy of the measured values. View the measured values on the relay in:

Actual Values > A2 Metering > Current

5A Secondary

Injected Current 5A unit (A)	CT Primary	Expected Current Reading	Measured Current Phase A	Measured Current Phase B	Measured Current Phase C
0.5					
1.0					
2.5					
5.0					
7.5					
10.0					

1A Secondary

Injected Current 1A unit (A)	CT Primary	Expected Current Reading	Measured Current Phase A	Measured Current Phase B	Measured Current Phase C
0.1					
0.2					
0.5					
1.0					
1.5					
2.0					

Voltage Input Accuracy Test

The 750/760 specifications for voltage input accuracy is ±0.25% of full scale (11 to 130 V) and ±0.8% of full scale (130 to 273 V). For open delta, the calculated phase has errors 2 times those shown. Perform the steps below to verify accuracy.

1. Determine the VT connection type from the relay settings file. (Wye or Delta)
2. Determine the voltage transformer ratio from the relay settings file.
3. Inject the values shown in the table below and verify accuracy of the measured values. View the measured values on the relay in:

Actual Values > A2 Metering > Voltage

wye connection

Applied Line-Neutral Voltage (V)	Expected Voltage Reading	Measured Voltage A-N	Measured Voltage B-N	Measured Voltage C-N
30				
50				
100				
150				
200				
270				

delta connection

Applied Line-Neutral Voltage (V)	Expected Voltage Reading	Measured Voltage A-B	Measured Voltage B-C	Measured Voltage C-A
30				
50				
100				
150				
200				
270				

Ground (5 A or 1 A) and Neutral Current Accuracy Test

The 750/760 specification for ground current input accuracy is +/- 0.5% of 2 × CT. Perform the steps below to verify accuracy.

5 A Input

1. Determine the Ground CT Primary amperage and the Phase Differential CT Primary amperage from the relay settings file.

2. Measured values should be +/-2.5 A. Inject the values shown in the table below and verify accuracy of the measured values. View the measure values on the relay in:

A2 Metering Data > Current Metering

5 A Secondary

Injected Current 5 A unit (A)	CT Primary	Expected Current Reading	Measured Ground Current
0.5			
1.0			
2.5			
5.0			
7.5			
10.0			

1 A Secondary

Injected Current 1 A unit (A)	CT Primary	Expected Current Reading	Measured Ground Current
0.1			
0.2			
0.5			
1.0			
1.5			
2.0			

Digital Inputs

The inputs can be verified easily with a simple switch or pushbutton. Verify the SWITCH +24 V DC with a voltmeter.   Perform the steps below to verify functionality of the hardware inputs. Ensure the relay is isolated from the system when performing these tests.

1. Open switches of all of the hardware inputs.
2. View the status of the hardware inputs:

Actual Values > A1 Status > Hardware Inputs

3. Close switches of all of the hardware inputs.
4. View the status of the hardware inputs:

Actual Values > A1 Status > Hardware Inputs

Contact #	Expected Status (Switch Open)	Pass / Fail	Expected Status (Switch Closed)	Pass/Fail
1	Open		Shorted	
2	Open		Shorted	
3	Open		Shorted	
4	Open		Shorted	
5	Open		Shorted	
6	Open		Shorted	
7	Open		Shorted	
8	Open		Shorted	
9	Open		Shorted	
10	Open		Shorted	
11	Open		Shorted	
12	Open		Shorted	
13	Open		Shorted	
14	Open		Shorted	

Analog Inputs and Outputs

The 750/760 specification for analog input and analog output accuracy is +/-1% of full scale. Perform the steps below to verify accuracy. Verify the Analog Input +24 V DC with a voltmeter. Determine from the relay settings file whether analog input is a 4 to 20 mA input range or a 0 to 1 mA input range, and use the appropriate test table.

4 to 20mA Analog Input – Start with Analog Input #1

1. Determine the type, Analog Input1 Minimum, and Analog Input1 Maximum from the relay settings file.
2. Analog output values should be +/- 0.2 mA on the ammeter. Measured analog input values should be +/- 10 units. Force the analog outputs using the following setpoints:

Setpoints > S8 Testing > Analog Outputs > Force Analog Outputs Function: "ENABLED"

Setpoints > S8 Testing > Analog Outputs > Force A/O 1: "0%"

(Enter desired value in percent; repeat for Analog Outputs 2 through 8)

3. Verify the ammeter readings as well as the measured analog input readings. For the purposes of testing, the analog input is fed in from the analog output. View the measured values in:

Actual Value > A2 Metering > Analog Input

Analog Output Force Value (%)	Expected Ammeter Reading (mA)	Measured Ammeter Reading (mA)				Expected Analog Input Reading	Measure Analog Input Reading (units)			
		1	2	3	4		1	2	3	4
0%	4									
25%	8									
50%	12									
75%	16									
100%	20									

0 to 1mA Analog Input – Start with Analog Input #1

1. Determine the type, Analog Input1 Minimum, and Analog Input1 Maximum from the relay settings file.
2. Analog output values should be +/- 0.01 mA on the ammeter. Measured analog input values should be +/- 10 units. Force the analog outputs using the following setpoints:

Setpoints > S8 Testing > Analog Outputs > Force Analog Outputs Function: "ENABLED"

Setpoints > S8 Testing > Analog Outputs > Force A/O 1: "0%"

(Enter desired value in percent; repeat for Analog Outputs 2 through 8)

3. Verify the ammeter readings as well as the measured analog input readings. For the purposes of testing, the analog input is fed in from the analog output. View the measured values in:

Actual Value > A2 Metering > Analog Input

Analog Output Force Value (%)	Expected Ammeter Reading (mA)	Measured Ammeter Reading (mA)				Expected Analog Input Reading	Measure Analog Input Reading (units)			
		1	2	3	4		1	2	3	4
0%	0									
25%	0.25									
50%	0.50									
75%	0.75									
100%	1.00									

Output Relays

Ensure the relay is isolated from the system when performing these tests.

To verify the functionality of the output relays, perform the following steps:

1. Enable the relay to test the outputs by enabling the 'force output' function. This can be done in:

Setpoints > S8 Testing > Output Relays > Force Output Relays Function: "ENABLED"

2. Force the state of each output relay to be de-energized. This can be done by:

Setpoints > S8 Testing > Output Relays > Force 1 Trip Relay: "DE-ENERGIZED"

Repeat step 2 for outputs 2 to 8 and for the Solid State Output.

3. Verify and record the state of each of the relays in the below table
4. Force the state of each output relay to be energized. This can be done by:

Setpoints > S8 Testing > Output Relays > Force 1 Trip Relay: "ENERGIZED"

Repeat step 4 for outputs 2 to 8 and for the Solid State Output.

5. Verify and record the state of each of the relays in the below table:

Forced Operation	Expected	Actual	Expected	Actual
1 Trip	De-Energized		Energized	
2 Close Relay	De-Energized		Energized	
3 Auxiliary	De-Energized		Energized	
4 Auxiliary	De-Energized		Energized	
5 Auxiliary	De-Energized		Energized	
6 Auxiliary	De-Energized		Energized	
7 Auxiliary	De-Energized		Energized	
8 Self Test	De-Energized		Energized	
Solid State Output	De-Energized		Energized	

Multilin 469

Motor Protection

Maintenance Guide

469 Maintenance Guide

Prior to maintenance on a relay, one should check if any service bulletins or product advisories exist for the relays in questions. This information can be found on the GE Multilin website or automatically downloaded from the EnerVista™ Launchpad document library.

If service bulletins or product advisories exist, the recommended remedial action should be implemented. Contact GE Multilin if any questions exist.

www.GEMultilin.com. 1-800-547-8629.

Recommended Tests

In-service maintenance:

1. Visual verification of analog value integrity such as voltage and current. Comparing metered values of the device with that of a corresponding system or device.
2. Visual verification of active alarms, relay display messages, self-test alarm messages, and LED indications.
3. LED test.
4. Visual inspection on relay physical condition, noting any damage, corrosion, excessive dust, or loose wires.
5. Event recorder file download with further events analysis to compare and verify recorded data corresponds with other independently verified event information.
6. Download relay settings file and check against the settings on record.

Out-of-service maintenance:

Prior to taking the relay out-of-service, it is recommended to perform the following In-service test:

1. Visual verification of active alarms, relay display messages, self-test alarm messages, and LED indications.
2. Visual inspection on relay physical condition, noting any damage, corrosion, excessive dust, or loose wires.
3. Event recorder file download with further events analysis to compare and verify recorded data corresponds with other independently verified event information.

For the following tests, the relay should be taken out-of-service.

1. Physically check wiring connections for integrity and inspect relay guide clips, shorting clips for wear and damage.
2. Analog values injection test (currents, voltages, RTDs, analog inputs) and metering accuracy verification. Tests the following hardware: CT inputs, ground inputs, low pass filters, sample and hold buffers, zero-crossing circuitry and multiplexer. Calibrated test equipment is required.
3. Test each relay communication port using the 469 Setup program and verify functionality of RS232, RS485, and if applicable Ethernet transceivers.

4. Setting change history using Viewpoint Maintenance software.

5. As-is settings comparison with as-left setting files using the 469 Setup software.

6. Secondary injection testing of AC quantities, DC signals to verify correct measurements are displayed.

7. Contact inputs and outputs verification. This test can be conducted by direct change of state forcing or as part of the system functional testing. Test Trip/Close coil monitors, logic inputs, solid-state outputs, output relays, analog outputs, and D/A converter.

8. LED Test and pushbutton continuity check.

9. Keypad test to verify that each key responds to key press.

10. 20 second control power removal to test Super-cap / battery backup by verifying relay date and time match before and after loss of power.

If these routine tests show that any element of the relay is defective, we recommend that GE Multilin be contacted to discuss the issue and make recommendations. Depending on the nature of the failure, it is not always necessary to remove the relay from service.

Unscheduled maintenance:

There are several events that may result in unscheduled maintenance being required on a protective relay, including:

- Relay self-test errors or spontaneous hardware failure.

- Unexpected protection operation for an external fault that otherwise should not have resulted in tripping.

- Failure of protection to trip for an internal fault that resulted in the operation of an upstream protection to clear the fault.

In all cases where there is a relay failure or inappropriate relay response, GE Multilin CST (Customer Service Team) should be contacted for technical support, including relay repair and detailed event analysis.

Self-Test Message Evaluation

Routine maintenance on the 469 should begin with an evaluation of any Diagnostic Messages of the relay either through the front panel, or remotely through the EnerVista™ Software program. The 469 relays perform self-test diagnostics at initialization and continuously as a background task. This ensures every testable component of the hardware and software is functioning correctly. There are two types of warnings displayed when the self-test detects a problem:

Major Problem: a serious problem that compromises all aspects of relay operation.
Minor Problem: a problem with the relay that does not compromise protection.

Diagnostic messages are automatically displayed for any active conditions in the relay such as trips, alarms, or asserted logic inputs. These messages provide a summary of the present state of the relay. The Message LED flashes when there are diagnostic messages present.

Self Test Message	Component / Function Affected	Severity	Failure Description
Self-Test Warning 1 Replace Immediately	Flash Memory Corruption	Major	Caused by detection of a corrupted location in the program memory. Every relay function is at risk of malfunctioning due to this memory error
Self-Test Warning 2 Replace Immediately	A/D Converter	Major	Caused by a failure of the analog to digital converter. The integrity of system essential input measurements is affected by this failure.
Self-Test Warning 3 Replace Immediately	A/D Converter	Major	Caused by a failure of the analog to digital converter. The integrity of system essential input measurements is affected by this failure.
Self-Test Warning 4 Replace Immediately	EEPROM Data Memory Corruption	Major	Corrupted location(s) in the relay data memory has been detected, which cannot be self-corrected. Every relay function is at risk of malfunctioning due to this memory error.
Self-Test Warning 5 Replace Immediately	10 Ohm Copper RTD #13	Major	Caused by out of range reading of self-test RTD 13. The integrity of system essential input measurements is affected by this failure.
Self-Test Warning 6 Replace Immediately	10 Ohm Copper RTD #14	Major	Caused by out of range reading of self-test RTD 14. The integrity of system essential input measurements is affected by this failure.
Self-Test Warning 7 Replace Immediately	10 Ohm Copper RTD #15	Major	Caused by out of range reading of self-test RTD 15. The integrity of system essential input measurements is affected by this failure.
Self-Test Warning 8 Replace Immediately	10 Ohm Copper RTD #16	Major	Caused by out of range reading of self-test RTD 16. The integrity of system essential input measurements is affected by this failure.
Clock Not Set Program Date/Time	Time Stamping & Synchronization	Minor	Occurs if the internal clock has not been set.
Unit Temp. Exceeded Service/Check Ambient	Extreme internal temperatures lead to component failure	Minor	Caused by the detection of unacceptably low temperatures (less than −40°C) or unacceptably high temperatures (greater than +85°C) detected inside the relay.
Relay Not Configured Consult User Manual	Current readings will be zero	Minor	Occurs when the 469 CT Primary or FLA is set to NONE.
Service Required Schedule Maintenance	Real Time Clock Crystal Failure	Minor	Caused by a failure of the Real Time Clock circuit. The ability of the relay to maintain the current date and time is lost.

469 Maintenance Worksheet

Hardware Functional Tests

Device Summary	
Device Name:	
Device Type:	
Order Code:	
Firmware Version:	
Serial Number:	
IP Address:	
Modbus Slave Address:	

Settings Summary	
Setting File Name:	
Last Changed:	
Changed by Whom (MAC Address)	

Do not change relay setting in order to perform maintenance testing on relays that have been commissioned.

Download the relay settings file and have these values available to conduct the following functional tests.

Phase Current Accuracy Test

The 469 specification for phase current accuracy is +/- 0.5% of 2 × CT when the injected current is less than 2 × CT. Perform the steps below to verify accuracy.

1. Determine the Phase CT Primary amperage from the relay settings file.
2. Inject the values shown in the table below and verify accuracy of the measured values. View the measured values on the relay in:

A2 Metering Data > Current Metering

5A Secondary

Injected Current 5A unit (A)	CT Primary	Expected Current Reading	Measured Current Phase A	Measured Current Phase B	Measured Current Phase C
0.5					
1.0					
2.5					
5.0					
7.5					
10.0					

1A Secondary

Injected Current 1A unit (A)	CT Primary	Expected Current Reading	Measured Current Phase A	Measured Current Phase B	Measured Current Phase C
0.1					
0.2					
0.5					
1.0					
1.5					
2.0					

Voltage Input Accuracy Test

The 469 specification for voltage input accuracy is +/- 0.5% of full scale (273 V). Perform the steps below to verify accuracy.

1. Determine the VT connection type from the relay settings file. (Wye or Delta)
2. Determine the voltage transformer ratio from the relay settings file.
3. Inject the values shown in the table below and verify accuracy of the measured values. View the measured values on the relay in:

A2 Metering Data > Voltage Metering

wye connection

Applied Line-Neutral Voltage (V)	Expected Voltage Reading	Measured Voltage A-N	Measured Voltage B-N	Measured Voltage C-N
30				
50				
100				
150				
200				
270				

delta connection

Applied Line-Neutral Voltage (V)	Expected Voltage Reading	Measured Voltage A-B	Measured Voltage B-C	Measured Voltage C-A
30				
50				
100				
150				
200				
270				

Ground Differential Accuracy Test

The 469 specification for differential current and 1 A/5 A ground current input accuracy is +/- 0.5% of 1 × CT for the 5A and 0.5% of 5 × CT for the 1 A input.

5 A Input

1. Determine the Ground CT Primary amperage and the Phase Differential CT Primary amperage from the relay settings file.

2. Measured values should be +/-5 A. Inject the values shown in the table below and verify accuracy of the measured values. View the measure values on the relay in:

A2 Metering Data > Current Metering

Injected Current 5 A unit (A)	CT Primary	Expected Current Reading	Measured Ground Current
0.5			
1.0			
2.5			
5.0			

1 A Input

1. Determine the Ground CT Primary amperage and the Phase Differential CT Primary amperage from the relay settings file.

2. Measured values should be +/-2.5 A. Inject the values shown the table below and verify accuracy of the measured values. View the measure values on the relay in:

A2 Metering Data > Current Metering

Injected Current 1 A unit (A)	CT Primary	Expected Current Reading	Measured Ground Current
0.1			
0.2			
0.5			
1.0			

GE Multilin 50:0.025 Ground Accuracy Test

The 469 specification for GE Multilin 50:0.025 ground current input accuracy is +/- 0.5% of CT rate primary (25A). Perform the steps below to verify accuracy.

5 A Input

1. Verify that the Ground CT is set to 50:0.025. If not, then this test should not be performed.

2. Measured values should be +/-0.125 A. Inject the values shown in the table below either as primary values into a GE Multilin 50:0.025 Core Balance CT or as secondary values that simulate the core balance CT. Verify accuracy of the measured values. View the measured values in:

A2 Metering Data > Current Metering

Primary Injected Current (A)	Secondary Injected Current (mA)	Expected Current Reading (A)	Measured Ground Current (A)
0.25	0.125	0.25	
1.0	0.5	1.00	
10.0	5	10.00	
25.0	12.5	25.00	

RTD Accuracy Test

The 469 specification for RTD input accuracy is +/- 2°C. Perform the steps below.

1. Determine the Stator RTD Type from the relay settings file.
2. Determine the RTD #1 Application type from the relay settings files.
3. Measured values should be +/-2°C or +/-4°F. After resistances applied to the RTD inputs as per the table below to simulate RTDs and verify accuracy of the measured values. View the measure values on the relay in:

A2 Metering Data > Temperature

Repeat these steps for RTDs #2 to #12.

Applied Resistance 100 Ω Platinum	Expected RTD Temperature Reading		Measured RTD Temperature Select One: _____°C _____°F											
	° Celsius	° Fahrenheit	1	2	3	4	5	6	7	8	9	10	11	12
80.31	-50	-58												
100.00	0	32												
119.39	50	122												
138.50	100	212												
157.32	150	302												
175.84	200	392												
194.08	250	482												

Applied Resistance 120 Ω Nickel	Expected RTD Temperature Reading		Measured RTD Temperature Select One: _____°C _____°F											
	° Celsius	° Fahrenheit	1	2	3	4	5	6	7	8	9	10	11	12
86.17	-50	-58												
120.00	0	32												
157.74	50	122												
200.64	100	212												
248.95	150	302												
303.46	200	392												
366.53	250	482												

Applied Resistance 100 Ω Nickel	Expected RTD Temperature Reading		Measured RTD Temperature Select One: _____ °C _____ °F											
	° Celsius	° Fahrenheit	1	2	3	4	5	6	7	8	9	10	11	12
71.81	-50	-58												
100.00	0	32												
131.45	50	122												
167.2	100	212												
207.45	150	302												
252.88	200	392												
305.44	250	482												

Applied Resistance 10 Ω Cooper	Expected RTD Temperature Reading		Measured RTD Temperature Select One: _____ °C _____ °F											
	° Celsius	° Fahrenheit	1	2	3	4	5	6	7	8	9	10	11	12
7.1	-50	-58												
9.04	0	32												
10.97	50	122												
12.9	100	212												
14.83	150	302												
16.78	200	392												
18.73	250	482												

Digital Inputs and Trip Coil Supervision

The digital inputs and trip coil supervision can be verified easily with a simple switch or pushbutton. Verify the SWITCH +24 V DC with a voltmeter. Perform the steps below to verify functionality of the digital inputs. Ensure the relay is isolated from the system when performing these tests.

1. Open switches of all of the digital inputs and the trip coil supervision circuit.
2. View the status of the digital inputs and trip coil supervision in:

Actual Values > A1 Status > Digital Inputs

3. Close switches of all of the digital inputs and the trip supervision circuit.
4. View the status of the digital inputs and trip coil supervision in:

Actual Values > A1 Status > Digital Inputs

Input	Expected Status (Switch Open)	Pass / Fail	Expected Status (Switch Closed)	Pass/Fail
Access	Open		Shorted	
Test	Open		Shorted	
Starter Status	Open		Shorted	
Emergency Status	Open		Shorted	
Remote Reset	Open		Shorted	
Assignable Input 1	Open		Shorted	
Assignable Input 2	Open		Shorted	
Assignable Input 3	Open		Shorted	
Assignable Input 4	Open		Shorted	
Trip Coil Supervision	No Coil		Coil	

Analog Inputs and Outputs

The 469 specification for analog input and analog output accuracy is +/-1% of full scale. Perform the steps below to verify accuracy. Verify the Analog Input +24 V DC with a voltmeter. Determine from the relay settings file whether analog input is a 4 to 20 mA input range or a 0 to 1 mA input range, and use the appropriate test table.

4 to 20mA Analog Input – Start with Analog Input #1

1. Determine the type, Analog Input1 Minimum, and Analog Input1 Maximum from the relay settings file.

2. Analog output values should be +/- 0.2 mA on the ammeter. Measured analog input values should be +/- 10 units. Force the analog outputs using the following setpoints:

S13 Testing > Test Analog Output > Force Analog Outputs Function: "ENABLED"

   S13 Testing > Test Analog Output > Analog Output 1 Forced Value: "0%"

   (Enter desired value in percent; repeat for Analog Outputs 2 through 4)

3. Verify the ammeter readings as well as the measured analog input readings. For the purposes of testing, the analog input is fed in from the analog output (see 469 Instruction Manual for Secondary Injection Test Setup). View the measured values in:

A2 Metering Data > Analog Inputs

Analog Output Force Value (%)	Expected Ammeter Reading (mA)	Measured Ammeter Reading (mA)				Expected Analog Input Reading	Measure Analog Input Reading (units)			
		1	2	3	4		1	2	3	4
0%	4									
25%	8									
50%	12									
75%	16									
100%	20									

0 to 1mA Analog Input – Start with Analog Input #1

1. Determine the type, Analog Input1 Minimum, and Analog Input1 Maximum from the relay settings file.
2. Analog output values should be +/- 0.01 mA on the ammeter. Measured analog input values should be +/- 10 units. Force the analog outputs using the following setpoints:

S13 Testing > Test Analog Output > Force Analog Outputs Function: "ENABLED"

S13 Testing > Test Analog Output > Analog Output 1 Forced Value: "0%"

(Enter desired value in percent; repeat for Analog Outputs 2 through 4)

3. Verify the ammeter readings as well as the measured analog input readings. For the purposes of testing, the analog input is fed in from the analog output (see 469 Instruction Manual for Secondary Injection Test Setup). View the measured values in:

A2 Metering Data > Analog Inputs

Analog Output Force Value (%)	Expected Ammeter Reading (mA)	Measured Ammeter Reading (mA)				Expected Analog Input Reading	Measure Analog Input Reading (units)			
		1	2	3	4		1	2	3	4
0%	0									
25%	0.25									
50%	0.50									
75%	0.75									
100%	1.00									

Output Relays

Ensure the relay is isolated from the system when performing these tests.
To verify the functionality of the output relays, perform the following steps:

1. Using the setpoint:

   S13 Testing > Test Output Relays > Force Operation of Relays: "1 TRIP"

2. Using the above setpoint, individually select each of the other output relays, (2 Auxiliary, 3 Auxiliary, ...). Verify operation, and stores values as per the table below.

Select and store values as per table below verifying operation

Force Operation Setpoint	Expected Measurement Check For Short												Actual Measurement Check for Short											
	1		2		3		4		5		6		1		2		3		4		5		6	
	NO	NC	NO	NC	NO	NC	NO	NC	NO	NC	NO	NC	NO	NC	NO	NC	NO	NC	NO	NC	NO	NC	NO	NC
1 Trip	X			X		X		X		X	X													
2 Auxiliary		X	X			X		X		X	X													
3 Auxiliary		X		X	X			X		X	X													
4 Alarm		X		X		X	X			X	X													
5 Blocks Start		X		X		X		X	X		X													
6 Service		X		X		X		X		X		X												
All Relays	X		X		X		X		X			X												
No Relays		X		X		X		X		X	X													

Note: the 6 SERVICE relay is failsafe, or energized normally.
Operating the 6 SERVICE relay causes it to de-energize.

Multilin 745
Transformer Protection

Maintenance Guide

745 Maintenance Guide

Prior to maintenance on a relay, one should check if any service bulletins or product advisories exist for the relays in questions. This information can be found on the GE Multilin website or automatically downloaded from the EnerVista™ Launchpad document library.

If service bulletins or product advisories exist, the recommended remedial action should be implemented. Contact GE Multilin if any questions exist.

www.GEMultilin.com. 1-800-547-8629.

Recommended Tests

In-service maintenance:

1. Visual verification of analog value integrity such as voltage and current. Comparing metered values of the device with that of a corresponding system or device.
2. Visual verification of active alarms, relay display messages, self-test alarm messages, and LED indications.
3. LED test.
4. Visual inspection on relay physical condition, noting any damage, corrosion, excessive dust, or loose wires.
5. Event recorder file download with further events analysis to compare and verify recorded data corresponds with other independently verified event information.
6. Download relay settings file and check against the settings on record.

Out-of-service maintenance:

Prior to taking the relay out-of-service, it is recommended to perform the following In-service test:

1. Visual verification of active alarms, relay display messages, self-test alarm messages, and LED indications.
2. Visual inspection on relay physical condition, noting any damage, corrosion, excessive dust, or loose wires.
3. Event recorder file download with further events analysis to compare and verify recorded data corresponds with other independently verified event information.

For the following tests, the relay should be taken out-of-service.

1. Physically check wiring connections for integrity and inspect relay guide clips, shorting clips for wear and damage.
2. Analog values injection test (currents, voltages, RTDs) and metering accuracy verification. Tests the following hardware: CT inputs, ground inputs, low pass filters, sample and hold buffers, zero-crossing circuitry and multiplexer. Calibrated test equipment is required.
3. Test each relay communication port using the 745 Setup program and verify functionality of RS232, RS485, and if applicable Ethernet transceivers.

4. Setting change history using Viewpoint Maintenance software.

5. As-is settings comparison with as-left setting files using the 745 Setup software.

6. Secondary injection testing of AC quantities, DC signals to verify correct measurements are displayed.

7. Contact inputs and outputs verification. This test can be conducted by direct change of state forcing or as part of the system functional testing. Test Trip/Close coil monitors, logic inputs, solid-state outputs, output relays, analog outputs, and D/A converter.

8. LED Test and pushbutton continuity check.

9. Keypad test to verify that each key responds to key press.

10. 20 second control power removal to test Super-cap / battery backup by verifying relay date and time match before and after loss of power.

If these routine tests show that any element of the relay is defective, we recommend that GE Multilin be contacted to discuss the issue and make recommendations. Depending on the nature of the failure, it is not always necessary to remove the relay from service.

Unscheduled maintenance:

There are several events that may result in unscheduled maintenance being required on a protective relay, including:

*   Relay self-test errors or spontaneous hardware failure.

*   Unexpected protection operation for an external fault that otherwise should not have resulted in tripping.

*   Failure of protection to trip for an internal fault that resulted in the operation of an upstream protection to clear the fault.

In all cases where there is a relay failure or inappropriate relay response, GE Multilin CST (Customer Service Team) should be contacted for technical support, including relay repair and detailed event analysis.

Self-Test Message Evaluation

Routine maintenance on the 745 should begin with an evaluation of any Diagnostic Messages of the relay either through the front panel, or remotely through the EnerVista™ Software program. The 745 relays perform self-test diagnostics at initialization and continuously as a background task. This ensures every testable component of the hardware and software is functioning correctly. There are two types of warnings displayed when the self-test detects a problem:

> Major Problem: a serious problem that compromises all aspects of relay operation.
> Minor Problem: a problem with the relay that does not compromise protection.

Diagnostic messages are automatically displayed for any active conditions in the relay such as trips, alarms, or asserted logic inputs. These messages provide a summary of the present state of the relay. The Message LED flashes when there are diagnostic messages present.

Event Message	Target Message	Severity	Cause
EEPROM Memory	Self-Test Warning 2 Replace Immediately	Major	Caused by detection of corrupted location in the 745 data memory which cannot be self-corrected. Errors that can be automatically corrected are not indicated. Any function of the 745 is susceptible to maloperate from this failure.
Flexlogic Equation	Flexlogic Eqn Error Consult User Manual	Major	Caused by the detection of unacceptably low (less than – 40°C) or high (greater than +85°C) temperatures detected inside the unit
DSP Processor	Self-Test Warning 6 Replace Immediately	Major	Caused when communications with the internal digital signal processor is lost. Most of the monitoring capability of the 745 (including all measurement of current) will be lost.
Bad Xfmr Settings	Bad Xfmr Settings Consult User Manual	Major	Caused when the 745 determines that the transformer configuration programmed via setpoints does not correspond to a realistic physical system.
Logic Input Power	Self-Test Warning 0 Replace Immediately	Minor	Caused by failure of the +32 V DC power supply used to power dry contacts of logic inputs. Logic inputs using internal power are affected by this failure. This may be caused by an external connection which shorts this power supply to ground.
Analog Output Power	Self-Test Warning 1 Replace Immediately	Minor	Caused by failure of the +32 V DC power supply used to power analog outputs. Analog output currents are affected by this failure.
Clock Not Set	Clock Not Set Program Date/Time	Minor	Caused when the 745 detects that the real-time clock is not running. The current time and date will not be maintained. Normally occurs when clock backup power is lost and control power is removed from the 745. User must reprogram via the S1 745 SETUP ► ▼ CLOCK menu.
Int Temperature	Unit Temp. Exceeded ServiceCheckAmbient	Minor	The relay has detected an unacceptably low (< –40°C) or high (> 85°C) temperature inside the unit.
IRIG-B Signal	IRIG-B Error Consult User Manual	Minor	Caused when the IRIG-B signal type selected does not match the format code being injected into the IRIG-B terminals.
Setpt Access Denied	Setpoint Access Denied Consult User Manual	Minor	Caused when the passcode is entered incorrectly three times in a row from either the front panel or any of the communication ports. This error may be removed by entering the correct passcode.
Ambient Temperature	Amb. Temp. Exceeded Check Ambient	Minor	Caused when ambient temperature is out of range.(–50 to 250°C inclusive).

745 Maintenance Worksheet

Hardware Functional Tests

Device Summary	
Device Name:	
Device Type:	
Order Code:	
Firmware Version:	
Serial Number:	
IP Address:	
Modbus Slave Address:	

Settings Summary	
Setting File Name:	
Last Changed:	
Changed by Whom (MAC Address)	

> Do not change relay setting in order to perform maintenance testing on relays that have been commissioned.
>
> Download the relay settings file and have these values available to conduct the following functional tests.

Phase Current Accuracy Test

The 745 specification for phase current accuracy is +/- 0.01% of CT nominal when the injected current is less than 4 x CT. Perform the steps below to verify accuracy.

1. Determine the Phase CT Primary amperage from the relay settings file/order code for each winding.

2. Inject the values shown in the table below and verify accuracy of the measured values for each winding connected. View the measured values on the relay in:

Actual Values > A2 Metering > Current > Winding Currents

5A Secondary

Injected Current 5A unit (A)	CT Primary	Expected Current Reading	Measured Current Phase A	Measured Current Phase B	Measured Current Phase C
0.5					
1.0					
2.5					
5.0					
7.5					
10.0					

1A Secondary

Injected Current 1A unit (A)	CT Primary	Expected Current Reading	Measured Current Phase A	Measured Current Phase B	Measured Current Phase C
0.1					
0.2					
0.5					
1.0					
1.5					
2.0					

Voltage Input Accuracy Test

The 745 specifications for voltage input accuracy is ±2.0% of full scale. For open delta, the calculated phase has errors 2 times those shown. Perform the steps below to verify accuracy.

1. Determine the VT connection type from the relay settings file. (Wye or Delta)
2. Determine the voltage transformer ratio from the relay settings file.
3. Inject the values shown in the table below and verify accuracy of the measured values. View the measured values on the relay in:

Actual Values > A2 Metering > Voltage

wye connection

Applied Line-Neutral Voltage (V)	Expected Voltage Reading	Measured Voltage
30		
50		
100		
150		
200		
270		

delta connection

Applied Line-Neutral Voltage (V)	Expected Voltage Reading	Measured Voltage
30		
50		
100		
150		
200		
270		

Ground (5 A or 1 A) Current Accuracy Test

The 745 specification for ground current input accuracy is +/- 0.01% of CT. Perform the steps below to verify accuracy.

5 A Input

1. Determine the Ground CT Primary amperage and the Phase Differential CT Primary amperage from the relay settings file.

2. Inject the values shown in the table below and verify accuracy of the measured values. View the measured values on the relay in:

A2 Metering Data > Current Metering

5 A Secondary

Injected Current 5 A unit (A)	CT Primary	Expected Current Reading	Measured Ground Current
0.5			
1.0			
2.5			
5.0			
7.5			
10.0			

1 A Secondary

Injected Current 1 A unit (A)	CT Primary	Expected Current Reading	Measured Ground Current
0.1			
0.2			
0.5			
1.0			
1.5			
2.0			

Digital Inputs

The inputs can be verified easily with a simple switch or pushbutton. For applications with dry contacts, verify the SWITCH +32 V DC with a voltmeter. Perform the steps below to verify functionality of the hardware inputs. Ensure the relay is isolated from the system when performing these tests.

1. Open switches of all of the hardware inputs.
2. View the status of the hardware inputs:

Actual Values > A1 Status > Hardware Inputs

3. Close switches of all of the hardware inputs.
4. View the status of the hardware inputs:

Actual Values > A1 Status > Hardware Inputs

Contact #	Expected Status (Switch Open)	Pass / Fail	Expected Status (Switch Closed)	Pass/Fail
1	Not Asserted		Asserted	
2	Open		Shorted	
3	Open		Shorted	
4	Open		Shorted	
5	Open		Shorted	
6	Open		Shorted	
7	Open		Shorted	
8	Open		Shorted	
9	Open		Shorted	
10	Open		Shorted	
11	Open		Shorted	
12	Open		Shorted	
13	Open		Shorted	
14	Open		Shorted	
15	Open		Shorted	
16	Open		Shorted	

Analog Inputs and Outputs

The 745 specification for analog input and analog output accuracy is +/-1% of full scale. Perform the steps below to verify accuracy. Verify the Analog Input +24 V DC with a voltmeter. Determine from the relay settings file the configured input range, and use the appropriate test table.

4 to 20mA Analog Input – Start with Analog Input #1

1. Determine the type, Analog Input1 Minimum, and Analog Input1 Maximum from the relay settings file.
2. Analog output values should be +/- 0.2 mA on the ammeter. Measured analog input values should be +/- 10 units. Force the analog outputs using the following setpoints:

Setpoints > S8 Testing > Analog Outputs > Force Analog Outputs Function: "ENABLED"

Setpoints > S8 Testing > Analog Outputs > Force A/O 1: "0%"

(Enter desired value in percent; repeat for Analog Outputs 2 through 7)

3. Verify the ammeter readings as well as the measured analog input readings. For the purposes of testing, the analog input is fed in from the analog output. View the measured values in:

Actual Value > A2 Metering > Analog Input

Analog Output Force Value (%)	Expected Ammeter Reading (mA)	Measured Ammeter Reading (mA)				Expected Analog Input Reading	Measure Analog Input Reading (units)			
		1	2	3	4		1	2	3	4
0%	4									
25%	8									
50%	12									
75%	16									
100%	20									

0 to 1mA Analog Input – Start with Analog Input #1

1. Determine the type, Analog Input1 Minimum, and Analog Input1 Maximum from the relay settings file.

2. Analog output values should be +/- 0.01 mA on the ammeter. Measured analog input values should be +/- 10 units. Force the analog outputs using the following setpoints:

Setpoints > S8 Testing > Analog Outputs > Force Analog Outputs Function: "ENABLED"

Setpoints > S8 Testing > Analog Outputs > Force A/O 1: "0%"

(Enter desired value in percent; repeat for Analog Outputs 2 through 7)

3. Verify the ammeter readings as well as the measured analog input readings. For the purposes of testing, the analog input is fed in from the analog output. View the measured values in:

Actual Value > A2 Metering > Analog Input

Analog Output Force Value (%)	Expected Ammeter Reading (mA)	Measured Ammeter Reading (mA)				Expected Analog Input Reading	Measure Analog Input Reading (units)			
		1	2	3	4		1	2	3	4
0%	0									
25%	0.25									
50%	0.50									
75%	0.75									
100%	1.00									

0 to 5mA Analog Input – Start with Analog Input #1

1. Determine the type, Analog Input1 Minimum, and Analog Input1 Maximum from the relay settings file.
2. Analog output values should be +/- 0.01 mA on the ammeter. Measured analog input values should be +/- 10 units. Force the analog outputs using the following setpoints:

Setpoints > S8 Testing > Analog Outputs > Force Analog Outputs Function: "ENABLED"

Setpoints > S8 Testing > Analog Outputs > Force A/O 1: "0%"

(Enter desired value in percent; repeat for Analog Outputs 2 through 7)

3. Verify the ammeter readings as well as the measured analog input readings. For the purposes of testing, the analog input is fed in from the analog output. View the measured values in:

Actual Value > A2 Metering > Analog Input

Analog Output Force Value (%)	Expected Ammeter Reading (mA)	Measured Ammeter Reading (mA)				Expected Analog Input Reading	Measure Analog Input Reading (units)			
		1	2	3	4		1	2	3	4
0%	0									
25%	1.25									
50%	2.50									
75%	3.75									
100%	5.00									

0 to 10mA Analog Input – Start with Analog Input #1

1. Determine the type, Analog Input1 Minimum, and Analog Input1 Maximum from the relay settings file.

2. Analog output values should be +/- 0.01 mA on the ammeter. Measured analog input values should be +/- 10 units. Force the analog outputs using the following setpoints:

Setpoints > S8 Testing > Analog Outputs > Force Analog Outputs Function: "ENABLED"

Setpoints > S8 Testing > Analog Outputs > Force A/O 1: "0%"

(Enter desired value in percent; repeat for Analog Outputs 2 through 7)

3. Verify the ammeter readings as well as the measured analog input readings. For the purposes of testing, the analog input is fed in from the analog output. View the measured values in:

Actual Value > A2 Metering > Analog Input

Analog Output Force Value (%)	Expected Ammeter Reading (mA)	Measured Ammeter Reading (mA)				Expected Analog Input Reading	Measure Analog Input Reading (units)			
		1	2	3	4		1	2	3	4
0%	0									
25%	2.50									
50%	5.00									
75%	7.50									
100%	10.00									

0 to 20mA Analog Input – Start with Analog Input #1

1. Determine the type, Analog Input1 Minimum, and Analog Input1 Maximum from the relay settings file.
2. Analog output values should be +/- 0.01 mA on the ammeter. Measured analog input values should be +/- 10 units. Force the analog outputs using the following setpoints:

Setpoints > S8 Testing > Analog Outputs > Force Analog Outputs Function: "ENABLED"

Setpoints > S8 Testing > Analog Outputs > Force A/O 1: "0%"

(Enter desired value in percent; repeat for Analog Outputs 2 through 7)

3. Verify the ammeter readings as well as the measured analog input readings. For the purposes of testing, the analog input is fed in from the analog output. View the measured values in:

Actual Value > A2 Metering > Analog Input

Analog Output Force Value (%)	Expected Ammeter Reading (mA)	Measured Ammeter Reading (mA)				Expected Analog Input Reading	Measure Analog Input Reading (units)			
		1	2	3	4		1	2	3	4
0%	0									
25%	5.00									
50%	10.00									
75%	15.00									
100%	20.00									

Output Relays

Ensure the relay is isolated from the system when performing these tests.

To verify the functionality of the output relays, perform the following steps:

1. Enable the relay to test the outputs by enabling the 'force output' function. This can be done in:

Setpoints > S8 Testing > Output Relays > Force Output Relays Function: "ENABLED"

2. Force the state of each output relay to be de-energized. This can be done by:

Setpoints > S8 Testing > Output Relays > Output1: "DE-ENERGIZED"

Repeat step 2 for the remaining outputs.

3. Verify and record the state of each of the relays in the below table.
4. Force the state of each output relay to be energized. This can be done by:

Setpoints > S8 Testing > Output Relays > Output1: "ENERGIZED"

Repeat step 4 for the remaining outputs.

5. Verify and record the state of each of the relays in the below table:

Forced Operation	Expected	Actual	Expected	Actual
1 Trip/Solid State	De-Energized		Energized	
2 Trip	De-Energized		Energized	
3 Trip	De-Energized		Energized	
4 Trip	De-Energized		Energized	
5 Auxiliary	De-Energized		Energized	
6 Auxiliary	De-Energized		Energized	
7 Auxiliary	De-Energized		Energized	
8 Auxiliary	De-Energized		Energized	
Self-Test	De-Energized		Energized	

Multilin 489
Generator Protection

Maintenance Guide

489 Maintenance Guide

Prior to maintenance on a relay, one should check if any service bulletins or product advisories exist for the relays in questions. This information can be found on the GE Multilin website or automatically downloaded from the EnerVista™ Launchpad document library.

If service bulletins or product advisories exist, the recommended remedial action should be implemented. Contact GE Multilin if any questions exist.

www.GEMultilin.com. 1-800-547-8629.

Recommended Tests

In-service maintenance:

1. Visual verification of analog value integrity such as voltage and current. Comparing metered values of the device with that of a corresponding system or device.
2. Visual verification of active alarms, relay display messages, self-test alarm messages, and LED indications.
3. LED test.
4. Visual inspection on relay physical condition, noting any damage, corrosion, excessive dust, or loose wires.
5. Event recorder file download with further events analysis to compare and verify recorded data corresponds with other independently verified event information.
6. Download relay settings file and check against the settings on record.

Out-of-service maintenance:

Prior to taking the relay out-of-service, it is recommended to perform the following In-service test:

1. Visual verification of active alarms, relay display messages, self-test alarm messages, and LED indications.
2. Visual inspection on relay physical condition, noting any damage, corrosion, excessive dust, or loose wires.
3. Event recorder file download with further events analysis to compare and verify recorded data corresponds with other independently verified event information.

For the following tests, the relay should be taken out-of-service.

1. Physically check wiring connections for integrity and inspect relay guide clips, shorting clips for wear and damage.
2. Analog values injection test (currents, voltages, RTDs, analog inputs) and metering accuracy verification. Tests the following hardware: CT inputs, ground inputs, low pass filters, sample and hold buffers, zero-crossing circuitry and multiplexer. Calibrated test equipment is required.
3. Test each relay communication port using the 489 Setup program and verify functionality of RS232, RS485, and if applicable Ethernet transceivers.

4. Setting change history using Viewpoint Maintenance software.

5. As-is settings comparison with as-left setting files using the 489 Setup software.

6. Secondary injection testing of AC quantities, DC signals to verify correct measurements are displayed.

7. Contact inputs and outputs verification. This test can be conducted by direct change of state forcing or as part of the system functional testing. Test Trip/Close coil monitors, logic inputs, solid-state outputs, output relays, analog outputs, and D/A converter.

8. LED Test and pushbutton continuity check.

9. Keypad test to verify that each key responds to key press.

10. 20 second control power removal to test Super-cap / battery backup by verifying relay date and time match before and after loss of power.

If these routine tests show that any element of the relay is defective, we recommend that GE Multilin be contacted to discuss the issue and make recommendations. Depending on the nature of the failure, it is not always necessary to remove the relay from service.

Unscheduled maintenance:

There are several events that may result in unscheduled maintenance being required on a protective relay, including:

- Relay self-test errors or spontaneous hardware failure.

- Unexpected protection operation for an external fault that otherwise should not have resulted in tripping.

- Failure of protection to trip for an internal fault that resulted in the operation of an upstream protection to clear the fault.

In all cases where there is a relay failure or inappropriate relay response, GE Multilin CST (Customer Service Team) should be contacted for technical support, including relay repair and detailed event analysis.

Self-Test Message Evaluation

Routine maintenance on the 489 should begin with an evaluation of any Diagnostic Messages of the relay either through the front panel, or remotely through the EnerVista™ Software program. The 489 relays perform self-test diagnostics at initialization and continuously as a background task. This ensures every testable component of the hardware and software is functioning correctly. There are two types of warnings displayed when the self-test detects a problem:

Major Problem: a serious problem that compromises all aspects of relay operation.
Minor Problem: a problem with the relay that does not compromise protection.

Diagnostic messages are automatically displayed for any active conditions in the relay such as trips, alarms, or asserted logic inputs. These messages provide a summary of the present state of the relay. The Message LED flashes when there are diagnostic messages present.

Self Test Message	Component / Function Affected	Severity	Failure Description
Self-Test Warning 1 Replace Immediately	Flash Memory Corruption	Major	Caused by detection of a corrupted location in the program memory. Every relay function is at risk of malfunctioning due to this memory error
Self-Test Warning 2 Replace Immediately	A/D Converter	Major	Caused by a failure of the analog to digital converter. The integrity of system essential input measurements is affected by this failure.
Self-Test Warning 3 Replace Immediately	A/D Converter	Major	Caused by a failure of the analog to digital converter. The integrity of system essential input measurements is affected by this failure.
Self-Test Warning 4 Replace Immediately	EEPROM Data Memory Corruption	Major	Corrupted location(s) in the relay data memory has been detected, which cannot be self-corrected. Every relay function is at risk of malfunctioning due to this memory error.
Self-Test Warning 5 Replace Immediately	10 Ohm Copper RTD #13	Major	Caused by out of range reading of self-test RTD 13. The integrity of system essential input measurements is affected by this failure.
Self-Test Warning 6 Replace Immediately	10 Ohm Copper RTD #14	Major	Caused by out of range reading of self-test RTD 14. The integrity of system essential input measurements is affected by this failure.
Self-Test Warning 7 Replace Immediately	10 Ohm Copper RTD #15	Major	Caused by out of range reading of self-test RTD 15. The integrity of system essential input measurements is affected by this failure.
Self-Test Warning 8 Replace Immediately	10 Ohm Copper RTD #16	Major	Caused by out of range reading of self-test RTD 16. The integrity of system essential input measurements is affected by this failure.
Clock Not Set Program Date/Time	Time Stamping & Synchronization	Minor	Occurs if the internal clock has not been set.
Unit Temp. Exceeded Service/Check Ambient	Extreme internal temperatures lead to component failure	Minor	Caused by the detection of unacceptably low temperatures (less than −40°C) or unacceptably high temperatures (greater than +85°C) detected inside the relay.
Relay Not Configured Consult User Manual	Current readings will be zero	Minor	Occurs when the 489 CT Primary or FLA is set to NONE.
Service Required Schedule Maintenance	Real Time Clock Crystal Failure	Minor	Caused by a failure of the Real Time Clock circuit. The ability of the relay to maintain the current date and time is lost.

489 Maintenance Worksheet

Hardware Functional Tests

Device Summary	
Device Name:	
Device Type:	
Order Code:	
Firmware Version:	
Serial Number:	
IP Address:	
Modbus Slave Address:	

Settings Summary	
Setting File Name:	
Last Changed:	
Changed by Whom (MAC Address)	

Do not change relay setting in order to perform maintenance testing on relays that have been commissioned.

Download the relay settings file and have these values available to conduct the following functional tests.

Phase Current Accuracy Test

The 489 specification for phase current accuracy is +/- 0.5% of 2 x CT when the injected current is less than 2 x CT. Perform the steps below to verify accuracy.

1. Determine the Phase CT Primary amperage from the relay settings file.
2. Inject the values shown the table below and verify accuracy of the measured values. View the measure values on the relay in:

A2 Metering Data > Current Metering

5A Secondary

Injected Current 5A unit (A)	CT Primary	Expected Current Reading	Measured Current Phase A	Measured Current Phase B	Measured Current Phase C
0.5					
1.0					
2.5					
5.0					
7.5					
10.0					

1A Secondary

Injected Current 1A unit (A)	CT Primary	Expected Current Reading	Measured Current Phase A	Measured Current Phase B	Measured Current Phase C
0.1					
0.2					
0.5					
1.0					
1.5					
2.0					

Voltage Input Accuracy Test

The 489 specification for voltage input accuracy is +/- 0.5% of full scale (200 V). Perform the steps below to verify accuracy.

1. Determine the VT connection type from the relay settings file. (Wye or Delta)
2. Determine the voltage transformer ratio from the relay settings file.
3. Inject the values shown the table below and verify accuracy of the measured values. View the measure values on the relay in:

A2 Metering Data > Voltage Metering

wye connection

Applied Line-Neutral Voltage (V)	Expected Voltage Reading	Measured Voltage A-N	Measured Voltage B-N	Measured Voltage C-N
30				
50				
100				
150				
200				

delta connection

Applied Line-Neutral Voltage (V)	Expected Voltage Reading	Measured Voltage A-B	Measured Voltage B-C	Measured Voltage C-A
30				
50				
100				
150				
200				

Ground (5A or 1A) and Neutral Current Accuracy Test

The 489 specification for neutral and ground current input accuracy is +/- 0.5% of 2 ×
CT. Perform the steps below to verify accuracy.

From the relay settings file, determine:

1. Ground CT setting. If it is 5A Secondary or 1A Secondary, proceed with this test.
   If it is 50:0.025, then proceed to the specific 50:0.025 Ground Current Accuracy
   Test.
2. Ground CT Ratio setting.
3. Phase CT Primary setting.
4. Phase Differential Trip setting. If set to "Latched" or "Unlatched", be aware that
   the trip element may operate.

Measured values should be +/-10 A. Inject (IA only) the values calculated in the table
below into one phase only and verify accuracy of the measured values.

View the measure values on the relay in:

A2 Metering Data > Current Metering

5A Secondary

Injected Current 5A unit (A)	CT Primary	Expected Current Reading	Measured Ground Current	Measured Neutral Current		
				Phase A	Phase B	Phase C
0.5						
1.0						
2.5						
5.0						
7.5						
10.0						

1A Secondary

Injected Current 5A unit (A)	CT Primary	Expected Current Reading	Measured Ground Current	Measured Neutral Current		
				Phase A	Phase B	Phase C
0.1						
0.2						
0.5						
1.0						
1.5						
2.0						

Neutral Voltage (Fundamental) Accuracy Test

The 489 specification for neutral voltage (fundamental) accuracy is +/- 0.5% of full scale (100V). Perform the steps below to verify accuracy.

1. Confirm from the relay that "Neutral Voltage Transformer = YES".
2. Confirm from the relay that "Generator Nominal Frequency = 60Hz".
3. Determine the "Neutral V.T. Ratio" from the relay settings file.
4. Measured values should be +/- 5.0 V. Apply the values shown in the table and verify accuracy of the measured values. View the measured values in:

A2 Metering Data > Voltage Metering

Applied Neutral Voltage at 60Hz (V)	Neutral VT Ratio	Expected Neutral Voltage (V)	Measured Neutral Voltage (V)
10			
30			
50			

GE Multilin 50:0.025 Ground Accuracy Test

The 489 specification for GE Multilin 50:0.025 ground current input accuracy is +/- 0.5% of CT rate primary (25A). Perform the steps below to verify accuracy.

1. Verify that the Ground CT is set to 50:0.025. If not, then this test should not be performed.
2. Measured values should be +/-0.25 A. Inject the values shown the table below either as primary values into a GE Multilin 50:0.025 Core Balance CT or as secondary values that simulate the core balance CT. Verify accuracy of the measure values. View the measured values in:

A2 Metering Data > Current Metering

Primary Injected Current (A)	Secondary Injected Current (mA)	Expected Current Reading (A)	Measured Ground Current (A)
0.25	0.125	0.25	
1.0	0.5	1.00	
5.0	2.5	5.00	
10.0	5.0	10.00	

RTD Accuracy Test

The 489 specification for RTD input accuracy is +/- 2° for Platinum/Nickel and +/- 5° for Copper. Perform the steps below.

1. Determine the Stator RTD Type from the relay settings file.
2. Determine the RTD #1 Application type from the relay settings files.
3. Measured values should be +/-2°C or +/-4°F for platinum/nickel and +/-5°C or +/-9°F for copper. After resistances applied to the RTD inputs as per the table below to simulate RTDs and verify accuracy of the measured values. View the measure values on the relay in:

A2 Metering Data > Temperature

Repeat these steps for RTDs #2 to #12.

Applied Resistance 100 Ω Platinum	Expected RTD Temperature Reading		Measured RTD Temperature Select One: _____ °C _____ °F											
	° Celsius	° Fahrenheit	1	2	3	4	5	6	7	8	9	10	11	12
84.27	-40	-40												
100.00	0	32												
119.39	50	122												
138.50	100	212												
157.32	150	302												
175.84	200	392												
194.08	250	482												

Applied Resistance 120 Ω Nickel	Expected RTD Temperature Reading		Measured RTD Temperature Select One: _____ °C _____ °F											
	° Celsius	° Fahrenheit	1	2	3	4	5	6	7	8	9	10	11	12
92.76	-40	-40												
120.00	0	32												
157.74	50	122												
200.64	100	212												
248.95	150	302												
303.46	200	392												
366.53	250	482												

Applied Resistance 100 Ω Nickel	Expected RTD Temperature Reading		Measured RTD Temperature Select One: _____ °C _____ °F											
	° Celsius	° Fahrenheit	1	2	3	4	5	6	7	8	9	10	11	12
77.30	-40	-40												
100.00	0	32												
131.45	50	122												
167.2	100	212												
207.45	150	302												
252.88	200	392												
305.44	250	482												

Applied Resistance 10 Ω Cooper	Expected RTD Temperature Reading		Measured RTD Temperature Select One: _____ °C _____ °F											
	° Celsius	° Fahrenheit	1	2	3	4	5	6	7	8	9	10	11	12
7.49	-40	-40												
9.04	0	32												
10.97	50	122												
12.9	100	212												
14.83	150	302												
16.78	200	392												
18.73	250	482												

Digital Inputs and Trip Coil Supervision

The digital inputs and trip coil supervision can be verified easily with a simple switch or pushbutton. Verify the SWITCH +24 V DC with a voltmeter. Perform the steps below to verify functionality of the digital inputs. Ensure the relay is isolated from the system when performing these tests.

1. Open switches of all of the digital inputs and the trip coil supervision circuit.
2. View the status of the digital inputs and trip coil supervision in:

Actual Values > A1 Status > Digital Inputs

3. Close switches of all of the digital inputs and the trip supervision circuit.
4. View the status of the digital inputs and trip coil supervision in:

Actual Values > A1 Status > Digital Inputs

Input	Expected Status (Switch Open)	Pass / Fail	Expected Status (Switch Closed)	Pass/Fail
Access	Open		Shorted	
Breaker Status	Open		Shorted	
Assignable Input 1	Open		Shorted	
Assignable Input 2	Open		Shorted	
Assignable Input 3	Open		Shorted	
Assignable Input 4	Open		Shorted	
Assignable Input 5	Open		Shorted	
Assignable Input 6	Open		Shorted	
Assignable Input 7	Open		Shorted	
Trip Coil Supervision	No Coil		Coil	

Analog Inputs and Outputs

The 489 specification for analog input and analog output accuracy is +/-1% of full scale. Perform the steps below to verify accuracy. Verify the Analog Input +24 V DC with a voltmeter. Determine from the relay settings file whether analog input is a 4 to 20 mA input range or a 0 to 1 mA input range, and use the appropriate test table.

4 to 20mA Analog Input – Start with Analog Input #1

1. Determine the type, Analog Input1 Minimum, and Analog Input1 Maximum from the relay settings file.
2. Analog output values should be +/- 0.2 mA on the ammeter. Measured analog input values should be +/- 10 units. Force the analog outputs using the following setpoints:

S12 Testing > Test Analog Output > Force Analog Outputs Function: "ENABLED"

S12 Testing > Test Analog Output > Analog Output 1 Forced Value: "0%"

(Enter desired value in percent; repeat for Analog Outputs 2 through 4)

3. Verify the ammeter readings as well as the measured analog input readings. For the purposes of testing, the analog input is fed in from the analog output (see 489 Instruction Manual for Secondary Injection Test Setup). View the measured values in:

A2 Metering Data > Analog Inputs

Analog Output Force Value (%)	Expected Ammeter Reading (mA)	Measured Ammeter Reading (mA)				Expected Analog Input Reading	Measure Analog Input Reading (units)			
		1	2	3	4		1	2	3	4
0%	4									
25%	8									
50%	12									
75%	16									
100%	20									

0 to 1mA Analog Input – Start with Analog Input #1

1. Determine the type, Analog Input1 Minimum, and Analog Input1 Maximum from the relay settings file.
2. Analog output values should be +/- 0.01 mA on the ammeter. Measured analog input values should be +/- 10 units. Force the analog outputs using the following setpoints:

S12 Testing > Test Analog Output > Force Analog Outputs Function: "ENABLED"

S12 Testing > Test Analog Output > Analog Output 1 Forced Value: "0%"

(Enter desired value in percent; repeat for Analog Outputs 2 through 4)

3. Verify the ammeter readings as well as the measured analog input readings. For the purposes of testing, the analog input is fed in from the analog output (see 489 Instruction Manual for Secondary Injection Test Setup). View the measured values in:

A2 Metering Data > Analog Inputs

Analog Output Force Value (%)	Expected Ammeter Reading (mA)	Measured Ammeter Reading (mA)				Expected Analog Input Reading	Measure Analog Input Reading (units)			
		1	2	3	4		1	2	3	4
0%	0									
25%	0.25									
50%	0.50									
75%	0.75									
100%	1.00									

Output Relays

Ensure the relay is isolated from the system when performing these tests.

To verify the functionality of the output relays, perform the following steps:

1. Using the setpoint:

   S12 Testing > Test Output Relays > Force Operation of Relays: "1 TRIP"

2. Using the above setpoint, individually select each of the other output relays, (2 Auxiliary, 3 Auxiliary, ...), Verify operation, and stores values as per the table below.

Select and store values as per table below verifying operation:

Force Operation Setpoint	Expected Measurement Check For Short												Actual Measurement Check for Short											
	1		2		3		4		5		6		1		2		3		4		5		6	
	NO	NC	NO	NC	NO	NC	NO	NC	NO	NC	NO	NC	NO	NC	NO	NC	NO	NC	NO	NC	NO	NC	NO	NC
1 Trip	X			X		X		X		X	X														
2 Auxiliary		X	X			X		X		X	X														
3 Auxiliary		X		X	X			X		X	X														
4 Auxiliary		X		X		X	X			X	X														
5 Alarm		X		X		X		X	X		X														
6 Service		X		X		X		X		X		X													
All Relays	X		X		X		X		X			X													
No Relays		X		X		X		X		X	X														

Note: the 6 SERVICE relay is failsafe, or energized normally.
Operating the 6 SERVICE relay causes it to de-energize.

Multilin 650 Family

Maintenance Guide

650 Maintenance Guide

Prior to maintenance on a relay, one should check if any service bulletins or product advisories exist for the relays in questions. This information can be found on the GE Multilin website or automatically downloaded from the EnerVista™ Launchpad document library.

If service bulletins or product advisories exist, the recommended remedial action should be implemented. Contact GE Multilin if any questions exist.

www.GEMultilin.com. 1-800-547-8629.

Recommended Tests

In-service maintenance:

1. Visual verification of analog value integrity such as voltage and current. Comparing metered values of the device with that of a corresponding system or device.
2. Visual verification of active alarms, relay display messages, self-test alarm messages, and LED indications.
3. LED test.
4. Visual inspection on relay physical condition, noting any damage, corrosion, excessive dust, or loose wires.
5. Event recorder file download with further events analysis to compare and verify recorded data corresponds with other independently verified event information.
6. Download relay settings file and check against the settings on record.

Out-of-service maintenance:

Prior to taking the relay out-of-service, it is recommended to perform the following In-service test:

1. Visual verification of active alarms, relay display messages, self-test alarm messages, and LED indications.
2. Visual inspection on relay physical condition, noting any damage, corrosion, excessive dust, or loose wires.
3. Event recorder file download with further events analysis to compare and verify recorded data corresponds with other independently verified event information.

For the following tests, the relay should be taken out-of-service.

1. Physically check wiring connections for integrity and inspect relay guide clips, shorting clips for wear and damage.
2. Analog values injection test (currents, voltages, analog inputs) and metering accuracy verification. Tests the following hardware: CT inputs, ground inputs, low pass filters, sample and hold buffers, zero-crossing circuitry and multiplexer. Calibrated test equipment is required.
3. Test each relay communication port using the EnerVista™ 650 Setup software and verify functionality of RS232, RS485, and if applicable Ethernet transceivers.

4. Setting change history using Viewpoint Maintenance software.

5. As-is settings comparison with as-left setting files using the EnerVista™ 650 Setup software.

6. Secondary injection testing of AC quantities, DC signals to verify correct measurements are displayed.

7. Contact inputs and outputs verification. This test can be conducted by direct change of state forcing or as part of the system functional testing. Test Trip/ Close coil monitors, logic inputs, output relays, and analog inputs.

8. LED Test and pushbutton continuity check.

9. Keypad test to verify that each key responds to key press.

If these routine tests show that any element of the relay is defective, we recommend that GE Multilin be contacted to discuss the issue and make recommendations. Depending on the nature of the failure, it is not always necessary to remove the relay from service.

Unscheduled maintenance:

There are several events that may result in unscheduled maintenance being required on a protective relay, including:

- Relay self-test errors or spontaneous hardware failure.

- Unexpected protection operation for an external fault that otherwise should not have resulted in tripping.

- Failure of protection to trip for an internal fault that resulted in the operation of an upstream protection to clear the fault.

In all cases where there is a relay failure or inappropriate relay response, GE Multilin CST (Customer Service Team) should be contacted for technical support, including relay repair and detailed event analysis.

Self-Test Message Evaluation

Routine maintenance on the 650 should begin with an evaluation of any Diagnostic Messages of the relay either through the front panel, or remotely through the EnerVista™ 650 Setup Software program. The 650 relays perform self-test diagnostics at initialization and continuously as a background task. This ensures every testable component of the hardware and software is functioning correctly. Refer to the relay user manual for more detail on any of the following diagnostic messages.

Critical: a serious problem that compromises all aspects of relay operation.

Non-Critical: a problem with the relay that does not compromise protection.

Diagnostic Message	Component / Function Affected	Severity	Description
DSP COMM ERROR: (0) or (1)	DSP Internal State	Critical	(0) Correct communications between DSP and main processor (1) Communication error between DSP and main processor
MAGNETIC MODULE ERROR: (0) or (1)	DSP Internal State	Critical	(0) Correct communications between DSP and magnetic module processor (1) Communication error between DSP and magnetic module processor
MAGNETIC MODULE ERROR: (0) or (1)	DSP Internal State	Critical	(0) Correct calibration values stored (1) Values are out of calibration limits
E2PROM STATUS: (0) or (1)	Flash Memory Internal State	Critical	(0) Not configured or problems during writing process (1) Configured and OK
BOARD F STATUS: (0) or (1)	I/O Board State	Critical	(0) Inactive - There is no communication with the board (1) Active - There is communication with the board
BOARD G STATUS: (0) or (1)	I/O Board State	Critical	(0) Inactive - There is no communication with the board (1) Active - There is communication with the board
BOARD H STATUS: (0) or (1)	I/O Board State	Critical	(0) Inactive - There is no communication with the board (1) Active - There is communication with the board
BOARD J STATUS: (0) or (1)	I/O Board State	Critical	(0) Inactive - There is no communication with the board (1) Active - There is communication with the board
ICD STATUS - UNKNOWN	IEC61850 Internal State	Non-Critical	When the relay model does not have IEC61850 protocol, the ICD status is unknown to the unit
ICD STATUS - ICD ERROR	IEC61850 Internal State	Non-Critical	There is an error in the ICD file and the relay ICD is not operative. Resolve this error using the IEC61850 configurator tool
ICD STATUS - MODIFIED	IEC61850 Internal State	Non-Critical	The settings have been changed in the ICD, but they are still not written in the relay ICD file
ICD STATUS - IN PROGRESS	IEC61850 Internal State	Non-Critical	The ICD settings are being written to the file in the relay
ICD STATUS - OK WITHOUT DAIS	IEC61850 Internal State	Non-Critical	The "Use DOI & DAI" setting has NOT been enabled and the relay is working properly with the ICD file
ICD STATUS - OK	IEC61850 Internal State	Non-Critical	The "Use DOI & DAI" setting has been enabled and the relay is working properly with the ICD file
USER MAP STATUS	Internal Relay State	Non-Critical	(0) Not configured (1) Configured

Diagnostic Message	Component / Function Affected	Severity	Description
FACTORY CALIBRATION	Internal Relay State	Non-Critical	(0) Not calibrated (1) Relay calibrated
FLEXCURVE A STATUS	Internal Relay State	Non-Critical	(0) Not configured (1) Configured
FLEXCURVE B STATUS	Internal Relay State	Non-Critical	(0) Not configured (1) Configured
FLEXCURVE C STATUS	Internal Relay State	Non-Critical	(0) Not configured (1) Configured
FLEXCURVE D STATUS	Internal Relay State	Non-Critical	(0) Not configured (1) Configured
Green Zone	Internal Relay State	Non-Critical	Memory internal status
Yellow Zone	Internal Relay State	Non-Critical	Memory internal status
Orange Zone	Internal Relay State	Non-Critical	Memory internal status
Red Zone	Internal Relay State	Non-Critical	Memory internal status
Up Time	Internal Relay State	Non-Critical	System running time since last reboot (ms)
SNTP FAILURE	Time Synchronization State	Non-Critical	Time Synchronization error occurring when: - no communication with SNTP time server - SNTP time server has invalid GPS source - incoming SNTP messages are corrupted
IRIGB FAILURE	Time Synchronization State	Non-Critical	Occurs when: - There is no IRIG-B signal connected to the relay - The IRIG-B signal connected to the relay is not valid

Note: It is advisable to use the critical alarms to raise an event or to light a warning LED for maintenance purposes.

650 Maintenance Worksheet

Hardware Functional Tests

Device Summary	
Device Name:	
Device Type:	
Order Code:	
Firmware Version:	
Serial Number:	
IP Address:	
Modbus Slave Address:	

Settings Summary	
Setting File Name:	
Last Changed:	
Changed by Whom (MAC Address)	

> Do not change relay setting in order to perform maintenance testing on relays that have been commissioned.
>
> Download the relay settings file and have these values available to conduct the following functional tests.

Phase Current Accuracy Test

The 650 relay family specification for phase current accuracy is +/- 0.5% of reading (+/- 10mA) from 0.05 to 10A and +/- 1.5% of reading (+/- 1mA) for values higher than 10A. Perform the steps below to verify accuracy.

1. Determine the Phase CT Primary amperage from the relay settings file.

2. Inject the values shown the table below and verify accuracy of the measured values. View the measured values on the relay in:

Actual > Metering > Primary Values > Current

5A Secondary

Injected Current 5A unit (A)	CT Primary	Expected Current Reading	Measured Current Phase A	Measured Current Phase B	Measured Current Phase C
0.5					
1.0					
2.5					
5.0					
7.5					
10.0					

1A Secondary

Injected Current 1A unit (A)	CT Primary	Expected Current Reading	Measured Current Phase A	Measured Current Phase B	Measured Current Phase C
0.1					
0.2					
0.5					
1.0					
1.5					
2.0					

Voltage Input Accuracy Test

F650

The F650 specification for voltage input accuracy is +/- 1% reading and +/- 0.1% Full Scale from 10V to 275V.

Perform the steps below to verify accuracy.

1. Determine the VT connection type from the relay settings file. (Wye or Delta)
2. Determine the voltage transformer ratio from the relay settings file.
3. Inject the values shown the table below and verify accuracy of the measured values. View the measure values on the relay in:

Actual > Metering > Primary Values > Voltage

wye connection

Applied Line-Neutral Voltage (V)	Expected Voltage Reading	Measured Voltage A-N	Measured Voltage B-N	Measured Voltage C-N
30				
50				
100				
150				
200				
275				

delta connection

Applied Line-Neutral Voltage (V)	Expected Voltage Reading	Measured Voltage A-B	Measured Voltage B-C	Measured Voltage C-A
30				
50				
100				
150				
200				
275				

G650 or W650

The G650 and W650 specification for voltage input accuracy is +/- 1% reading and +/- 0.1% Full Scale from 10V to 500V.

Perform the steps below to verify accuracy.

1. Determine the VT connection type from the relay settings file. (Wye or Delta)
2. Determine the voltage transformer ratio from the relay settings file.
3. Inject the values shown the table below and verify accuracy of the measured values. View the measure values on the relay in:

Actual > Metering > Primary Values > Voltage

wye connection

Applied Line-Neutral Voltage (V)	Expected Voltage Reading	Measured Voltage A-N	Measured Voltage B-N	Measured Voltage C-N
30				
50				
100				
150				
200				
300				
400				
500				

delta connection

Applied Line-Neutral Voltage (V)	Expected Voltage Reading	Measured Voltage A-B	Measured Voltage B-C	Measured Voltage C-A
30				
50				
100				
150				
200				
300				
400				
500				

Ground and Neutral Current Accuracy Test (5A or 1A)

The 650 relay family specification for ground current input accuracy and neutral current input accuracy is +/- 0.5% of reading (+/- 10mA) from 0.05 to 10A.

Perform the steps below to verify accuracy.

1. Determine the Ground CT Primary amperage from the relay settings file.
2. Determine the Neutral CT Primary amperage from the relay settings file.
3. Inject the values shown the table below and verify accuracy of the measured values. View the measured values on the relay in:

Actual>Metering > Primary Values > Current

5A Secondary

Injected Current 5A unit (A)	CT Primary	Expected Current Reading	Measured Ground Current	Measured Neutral Current		
				Phase A	Phase B	Phase C
0.5						
1.0						
2.5						
5.0						
7.5						
10.0						

1A Secondary

Injected Current 5A unit (A)	CT Primary	Expected Current Reading	Measured Ground Current	Measured Neutral Current		
				Phase A	Phase B	Phase C
0.1						
0.2						
0.5						
1.0						
1.5						
2.0						

Digital Inputs and Trip Coil Supervision

Depending on the relay model, the number of digital inputs can vary up to a maximum of 128.

The digital inputs and trip coil supervision can be verified easily with a simple switch or pushbutton. Verify the switch with an ohmmeter or continuity tester. Perform the steps below to verify functionality of the digital inputs. Ensure the relay is isolated from the system when performing these tests.

1. Open switches of all of the digital inputs and the trip coil supervision circuit.
2. View the status of the digital inputs and trip coil supervision in:

Actual > Inputs/Outputs > Contact inputs > Board 'X'
('X' corresponding to the board location)

3. Record whether the test was "Passed" or "Failed".
4. Close switches of all of the digital inputs and the trip supervision circuit.
5. View the status of the digital inputs and trip coil supervision in:

Actual > Inputs/Outputs > Contact inputs > Board 'X'
('X' corresponding to the board location)

6. Record whether the test was "Passed" or "Failed".

The I/O Board Location (X) options correspond to the following:

F for board in first slot

G for board in second slot

H for board in first slot of CIO module

J for board in second slot of CIO module

Input Type: refers to the type of logic associated to the physical input.

- Positive or Negative settings correspond to signals that re activated or deactivated with the input level, considering the delay setting.
- Positive-edge or Negative-edge settings correspond to signals that are activated with the change of the input signal. Delay Input Time will not be considered, only the Debounce Time.

Input Activation Voltage Threshold: The range of this value goes from 20 to 230 volts. There is a single setting for all inputs sharing the same common. In mixed and supervision boards there are two groups of inputs.

Input #	Board Location	Input Type	Voltage Threshold	Expected Status (Switch Open)	Pass / Fail	Expected Status (Switch Closed)	Pass/ Fail
				Open or No Coil		Shorted or Coil	
				Open or No Coil		Shorted or Coil	
				Open or No Coil		Shorted or Coil	
				Open or No Coil		Shorted or Coil	
				Open or No Coil		Shorted or Coil	
				Open or No Coil		Shorted or Coil	
				Open or No Coil		Shorted or Coil	
				Open or No Coil		Shorted or Coil	
				Open or No Coil		Shorted or Coil	
				Open or No Coil		Shorted or Coil	
				Open or No Coil		Shorted or Coil	
				Open or No Coil		Shorted or Coil	
				Open or No Coil		Shorted or Coil	
				Open or No Coil		Shorted or Coil	
				Open or No Coil		Shorted or Coil	
				Open or No Coil		Shorted or Coil	

If additional digital inputs exist, repeat these tests for remaining inputs.

Output Relays (Digital Outputs)

Ensure the relay is isolated from the system when performing these tests.

To verify the functionality of the output relays, perform the following steps:

1. Force the state of each output relay to be de-energized. This can be done by:

Setpoint > Inputs/Outputs > Force Outputs
('X' corresponding to the board location)

Repeat step 1 for the remaining outputs on all available boards.

2. Verify and record the state of each of the relays in the below table from:

Actual > Inputs/Outputs > Contact Output Status > Board 'X'

3. Force the state of each output relay to be energized. This can be done by:

Setpoint > Inputs/Outputs > Force Outputs

4. Verify and record the state of each of the relays in the below table from:

Actual > Inputs/Outputs > Contact Output Status > Board 'X'
('X' corresponding to the board location)

Input #	Board Location	Expected Status	Actual	Expected Status	Actual
		De-energized		Energized	
		De-energized		Energized	
		De-energized		Energized	
		De-energized		Energized	
		De-energized		Energized	
		De-energized		Energized	
		De-energized		Energized	
		De-energized		Energized	

Analog Inputs

The 650 specification for analog input accuracy is +/-2% of full scale. Perform the steps below to verify accuracy. Verify the Analog Input +24 V DC with a voltmeter.

Determine from the relay settings file what the analog input type is:

0 to -1mA	0 to +1mA	-1 to +1mA	0 to 5mA
0 to 10mA	0 to 20mA	4 to 20mA	

Start with Analog Input #1

1. Determine the type, Analog Input Minimum, and Analog Input Maximum from the relay settings file.
2. Determine the I/O board letter on which the analog inputs are located.
3. Calculate the required DCmA values based on the table below, and inject that value into the analog input.
4. Verify the ammeter readings as well as the measured analog input readings.
5. View the measured values in:

Actual > Inputs/Outputs > Analog Inputs > Board X

(X corresponding to the board location)

% of Analog Input Max to Inject	Analog Input #1		Analog Input #2		Analog Input #3		Analog Input #4	
	Type:		Type:		Type:		Type:	
	Expected Reading (units)	Measured Reading (units)	Expected Reading (units)	Measured Reading (units)	Expected Reading (units)	Measured Reading (units)	Expected Reading (units)	Measured Reading (units)
0%								
25%								
50%								
75%								
100%								

% of Analog Input Max to Inject	Analog Input #5		Analog Input #6		Analog Input #7		Analog Input #8	
	Type:		Type:		Type:		Type:	
	Expected Reading (units)	Measured Reading (units)	Expected Reading (units)	Measured Reading (units)	Expected Reading (units)	Measured Reading (units)	Expected Reading (units)	Measured Reading (units)
0%								
25%								
50%								
75%								
100%								

Multilin 350

Feeder Protection

Maintenance Guide

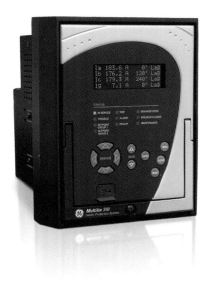

350 Maintenance Guide

Prior to maintenance on a relay, one should check if any service bulletins or product advisories exist for the relays in question. This information can be found on the GE Multilin website or automatically downloaded from the EnerVista™ Launchpad document library.

If service bulletins or product advisories exist, the recommended remedial action should be implemented. Contact GE Multilin if any questions exist.

GEDigitalEnergy.com. 1-800-547-8629.

Recommended Tests

In-service maintenance:

1. Visual verification of analog value integrity such as voltage and current. Comparing metered values of the device with that of a corresponding system or device.
2. Visual verification of active alarms, relay display messages, self-test alarm messages, and LED indications.
3. Visual inspection on relay physical condition, noting any damage, corrosion, excessive dust, or loose wires.
4. Event recorder file download with further events analysis to compare and verify recorded data corresponds with other independently verified event information.
5. Download relay settings file and check against the settings on record.

Out-of-service maintenance:

Prior to taking the relay out-of-service, it is recommended to perform the following In-service test:

1. Visual verification of active alarms, relay display messages, self-test alarm messages, and LED indications.
2. Visual inspection on relay physical condition, noting any damage, corrosion, excessive dust, or loose wires.
3. Event recorder file download with further events analysis to compare and verify recorded data corresponds with other independently verified event information.

For the following tests, the relay should be taken out-of-service.

1. Physically check wiring connections for integrity and inspect for damage.
2. Analog values injection test (currents, voltages) and metering accuracy verification. Tests the following hardware: CT inputs, ground inputs, low pass filters, sample and hold buffers, zero-crossing circuitry and multiplexer. Calibrated test equipment is required.
3. Test each relay communication port using the 350 Setup program and verify functionality of USB, RS485, and if applicable Ethernet transceivers.
4. Setting change history using Viewpoint Maintenance software.
5. As-is settings comparison with as-left setting files using the 350 Setup software.

6. Secondary injection testing of AC quantities, DC signals to verify correct measurements are displayed.

7. Contact inputs and outputs verification. This test can be conducted by direct change of state forcing or as part of the system functional testing.

8. Keypad test to verify that each key responds to key press.

9. 20 second control power removal to test Super-cap / backup by verifying relay date and time match before and after loss of power.

If these routine tests show that any element of the relay is defective, we recommend that GE Multilin be contacted to discuss the issue and make recommendations. Depending on the nature of the failure, it is not always necessary to remove the relay from service.

Unscheduled maintenance:

There are several events that may result in unscheduled maintenance being required on a protective relay, including:

- Relay self-test errors or spontaneous hardware failure.
- Unexpected protection operation for an external fault that otherwise should not have resulted in tripping.
- Failure of protection to trip for an external fault that resulted in the operation of an upstream protection to clear the fault.

In all cases where there is a relay failure or inappropriate relay response, GE Multilin CST (Customer Service Team) should be contacted for technical support, including relay repair and detailed event analysis.

Self-Test Message Evaluation

Routine maintenance on the 350 should begin with an evaluation of any Diagnostic Messages of the relay either through the front panel, or remotely through the EnerVista™ Software program. The 350 relays perform self-test diagnostics at initialization and continuously as a background task. This ensures every testable component of the hardware and software is functioning correctly. There are two types of warnings displayed when the self-test detects a problem:

Major Problem: a serious problem that compromises all aspects of relay operation.

Minor Problem: a problem with the relay that does not compromise protection.

Diagnostic messages are automatically displayed for any active conditions in the relay such as trips, alarms, or asserted logic element. These messages provide a summary of the present state of the relay. The Message LED flashes when there are diagnostic messages present.

Minor Self-test Errors

Self-test Error Message	Latched Target Message?	Description of Problem	How Often the Test is Performed	What to do
MAINTENANCE ALERT: IRIG-B Failure	No	A bad IRIG-B input signal has been detected.	Every 5 seconds*	Ensure IRIG-B cable is connected, check cable functionality (i.e. physical damage or perform continuity test), ensure IRIG-B receiver is functioning, and check input signal level (it may be less than specification). If none of these apply, contact the factory.
MAINTENANCE ALERT: Clock Not Set	No	Clock time is the same as the default time.	Every 5 seconds*	Set the date and time in PRODUCT SETUP.
MAINTENANCE ALERT: Comm Alert 1, 2, or 3	No	Communication error between CPU and Comms board.	Every 5 seconds*	If alert doesn't self-reset, then contact factory. Otherwise monitor reccurences as errors are detected and self-reset.
MAINTENANCE ALERT : Ethernet Link Fail	No	Communication error between 350 and Network.	Detected Instantaneously	Check Ethernet cable and Ethernet connection. Check health of the network. Check status of external routers and switches.

Major Self-test Errors

Self-test Error Message	Latched Target Message?	Description of Problem	How Often the Test is Performed	What to do
UNIT FAILURE: Contact Factory (XXXX)	Yes	This warning is caused by a unit hardware failure. Failure code (XXXX) is shown.	Every 5 seconds*	Contact the factory and provide the failure code.
RELAY NOT READY: Check Settings	No	PRODUCT SETUP INSTALLATION setting indicates that relay is not in a programmed state.	On power up and whenever the PRODUCT SETUP INSTALLATION setting is altered.	Program all required settings then set the PRODUCT SETUP INSTALLATION setting to "Ready"

* Failure is logged after the detection of 5 consecutive failures - that is, after 25 seconds.

350 Maintenance Worksheet

Hardware Functional Tests

Device Summary	
Device Name:	
Device Type:	
Order Code:	
Firmware Version:	
Serial Number:	
IP Address:	
Modbus Slave Address:	

Settings Summary	
Setting File Name:	
Last Changed:	
Changed by Whom (MAC Address)	

Do not change relay settings in order to perform maintenance testing on relays that have been commissioned.

Download the relay settings file and have these values available to conduct the following functional tests.

Phase Current Accuracy Test

The 350 specification for phase current accuracy is ±1% of reading at 1× CT, ±3% of reading from 0.2 to 20 × CT, ±20% of reading from 0.05 to 0.19 × CT. Perform the steps below to verify accuracy.

1. Determine the Phase CT Primary amperage from the relay settings file.
2. Inject the values shown in the table below and verify accuracy of the measured values. View the measured values on the relay in:

Actual Values > A2 Metering > Current

5A Secondary

Injected Current 5A unit (A)	CT Primary	Expected Current Reading	Measured Current Phase A	Measured Current Phase B	Measured Current Phase C
0.5					
1.0					
2.5					
5.0					
7.5					
10.0					

1A Secondary

Injected Current 1A unit (A)	CT Primary	Expected Current Reading	Measured Current Phase A	Measured Current Phase B	Measured Current Phase C
0.1					
0.2					
0.5					
1.0					
1.5					
2.0					

Voltage Input Accuracy Test

The 350 specifications for voltage input accuracy is +/- 1% of range. Voltage Range 50 to 240 V. Perform the steps below to verify accuracy.

1. Determine the VT connection type from the relay settings file. (Wye or Delta)
2. Determine the voltage transformer ratio from the relay settings file.
3. Inject the values shown in the table below and verify accuracy of the measured values. View the measured values on the relay in:

Actual Values > A2 Metering > Voltage

wye connection

Applied Line-Neutral Voltage (V)	Expected Voltage Reading	Measured Voltage A-N	Measured Voltage B-N	Measured Voltage C-N
50				
100				
150				
200				
240				

delta connection

Applied Line-Line Voltage (V)	Expected Voltage Reading	Measured Voltage A-B	Measured Voltage B-C	Measured Voltage C-A
50				
100				
150				
200				
240				

Ground (5 A or 1 A) and Neutral Current Accuracy Test

The 350 specification for ground current input accuracy is ±1% of reading at 1× CT, ±3% of reading from 0.2 to 20 × CT, ±20% of reading from 0.05 to 0.19 × CT. Perform the steps below to verify accuracy.

5 A Input

1. Determine the Ground CT Primary amperage from the relay settings file.

2. Inject the values shown in the table below and verify accuracy of the measured values. View the measured values on the relay in:

A2 Metering Data > Current Metering

5 A Secondary

Injected Current 5 A unit (A)	CT Primary	Expected Current Reading	Measured Ground Current
0.5			
1.0			
2.5			
5.0			
7.5			
10.0			

1 A Secondary

Injected Current 1 A unit (A)	CT Primary	Expected Current Reading	Measured Ground Current
0.1			
0.2			
0.5			
1.0			
1.5			
2.0			

Digital Inputs

The inputs can be verified easily with an external DC voltage supply. Perform the steps below to verify functionality of the hardware inputs. Ensure the relay is isolated from the system when performing these tests.

Actual Values > A1 Status > Contact Input

Contact #	Expected Status (Switch Open)	Pass / Fail	Expected Status (Switch Closed)	Pass/Fail
1	Open		Shorted	
2	Open		Shorted	
3	Open		Shorted	
4	Open		Shorted	
5	Open		Shorted	
6	Open		Shorted	
7	Open		Shorted	
8	Open		Shorted	
9	Open		Shorted	
10	Open		Shorted	

1. Program contact input threshold to 17 VDC
2. View the status of the hardware inputs
3. Contect DC Supply - to input common
4. Contect DC Supply + to input #1-10
5. View the status of the hardware input

Multilin 339
Motor Protection

Maintenance Guide

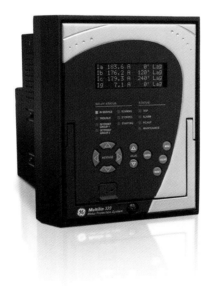

339 Maintenance Guide

Prior to maintenance on a relay, one should check if any service bulletins or product advisories exist for the relays in question. This information can be found on the GE Multilin website or automatically downloaded from the EnerVista™ Launchpad document library.

If service bulletins or product advisories exist, the recommended remedial action should be implemented. Contact GE Multilin if any questions exist.

www.GEMultilin.com. 1-800-547-8629.

Recommended Tests

In-service maintenance:

1. Visual verification of analog value integrity such as voltage and current. Comparing metered values of the device with that of a corresponding system or device.
2. Visual verification of active alarms, relay display messages, self-test alarm messages, and LED indications.
3. Visual inspection on relay physical condition, noting any damage, corrosion, excessive dust, or loose wires.
4. Event recorder file download with further events analysis to compare and verify recorded data corresponds with other independently verified event information.
5. Download relay settings file and check against the settings on record.

Out-of-service maintenance:

Prior to taking the relay out-of-service, it is recommended to perform the following In-service test:

1. Visual verification of active alarms, relay display messages, self-test alarm messages, and LED indications.
2. Visual inspection on relay physical condition, noting any damage, corrosion, excessive dust, or loose wires.
3. Event recorder file download with further events analysis to compare and verify recorded data corresponds with other independently verified event information.

For the following tests, the relay should be taken out-of-service.

1. Physically check wiring connections for integrity and inspect for damage.
2. Analog values injection test (currents, voltages, RTDs) and metering accuracy verification. Tests the following hardware: CT inputs, ground inputs, low pass filters, sample and hold buffers, zero-crossing circuitry and multiplexer. Calibrated test equipment is required.
3. Test each relay communication port using the 339 Setup program and verify functionality of USB, RS485, and if applicable Ethernet transceivers.
4. Setting change history using Viewpoint Maintenance software.
5. As-is settings comparison with as-left setting files using the 339 Setup software.

6. Secondary injection testing of AC quantities, DC signals to verify correct measurements are displayed.

7. Contact inputs and outputs verification. This test can be conducted by direct change of state forcing or as part of the system functional testing.

8. Keypad test to verify that each key responds to key press.

9. 20 second control power removal to test Super-cap / backup by verifying relay date and time match before and after loss of power.

If these routine tests show that any element of the relay is defective, we recommend that GE Multilin be contacted to discuss the issue and make recommendations. Depending on the nature of the failure, it is not always necessary to remove the relay from service.

Unscheduled maintenance:

There are several events that may result in unscheduled maintenance being required on a protective relay, including:

- Relay self-test errors or spontaneous hardware failure.

- Unexpected protection operation for an external fault that otherwise should not have resulted in tripping.

- Failure of protection to trip for an external fault that resulted in the operation of an upstream protection to clear the fault.

In all cases where there is a relay failure or inappropriate relay response, GE Multilin CST (Customer Service Team) should be contacted for technical support, including relay repair and detailed event analysis.

Self-Test Message Evaluation

Routine maintenance on the 339 should begin with an evaluation of any Diagnostic Messages of the relay either through the front panel, or remotely through the EnerVista™ Software program. The 339 relays perform self-test diagnostics at initialization and continuously as a background task. This ensures every testable component of the hardware and software is functioning correctly. There are two types of warnings displayed when the self-test detects a problem:

> Major Problem: a serious problem that compromises all aspects of relay operation.
> Minor Problem: a problem with the relay that does not compromise protection.

Diagnostic messages are automatically displayed for any active conditions in the relay such as trips, alarms, or asserted logic elements. These messages provide a summary of the present state of the relay.

Minor Self-test Errors

Self-test Error Message	Latched Target Message?	Description of Problem	How Often the Test is Performed	What to do
MAINTENANCE ALERT: IRIG-B Failure	No	A bad IRIG-B input signal has been detected.	Every 5 seconds*	Ensure IRIG-B cable is connected, check cable functionality (i.e. physical damage or perform continuity test), ensure IRIG-B receiver is functioning, and check input signal level (it may be less than specification). If none of these apply, contact the factory.
MAINTENANCE ALERT: Clock Not Set	No	Clock time is the same as the default time.	Every 5 seconds*	Set the date and time in PRODUCT SETUP.
MAINTENANCE ALERT: Comm Alert 1, 2, or 3	No	Communication error between CPU and Comms board.	Every 5 seconds*	If alert doesn't self-reset, then contact factory. Otherwise monitor reccurences as errors are detected and self-reset.
MAINTENANCE ALERT : Ethernet Link Fail	No	Communication error between 350 and Network.	Detected Instantaneously	Check Ethernet cable and Ethernet connection. Check health of the network. Check status of external routers and switches.
MAINTENANCE ALERT: High Ethernet Traffic	No		Every 5 seconds*	
MAINTENANCE ALERT: High Ambient Temperature	No	The ambient temperature is above 80oC.	Every 1 hour	Increase ventillation to the surroundings.
MAINTENANCE ALERT : RMIO Mismatch	No	RMIO Module is not validated; communications with the RMIO module are lost or interrupted.	Every 5 seconds*	Validate the RMIO Module; check CANBUS communication.

Major Self-test Errors

Self-test Error Message	Latched Target Message?	Description of Problem	How Often the Test is Performed	What to do
UNIT FAILURE: Contact Factory (XXXX)	Yes	This warning is caused by a unit hardware failure. Failure code (XXXX) is shown.	Every 5 seconds*	Contact the factory and provide the failure code.
RELAY NOT READY: Check Settings	No	S1 RELAY SETUP> INSTALLATION > RELAY STATUS is set to "Not Ready".	On power up and whenever the RELAY STATUS setting is altered.	Program all required settings then set the S1 RELAY SETUP > INSTALLATION > RELAY STATUS setting to "Ready".

* Failure is logged after the detection of 5 consecutive failures - that is, after 25 seconds.

339 Maintenance Worksheet

Hardware Functional Tests

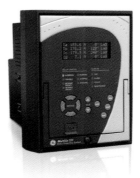

Device Summary	
Device Name:	
Device Type:	
Order Code:	
Firmware Version:	
Serial Number:	
IP Address:	
Modbus Slave Address:	

Settings Summary	
Setting File Name:	
Last Changed:	
Changed by Whom (MAC Address)	

Do not change relay settings in order to perform maintenance testing on relays that have been commissioned.

Download the relay settings file and have these values available to conduct the following functional tests.

Phase Current Accuracy Test

The 339 specification for phase current accuracy is ±1% of reading at 1× CT, ±3% of reading from 0.2 to 20 × CT, ±20% of reading from 0.05 to 0.19 × CT. Perform the steps below to verify accuracy.

1. Determine the Phase CT Primary amperage from the relay settings file.
2. Inject the values shown in the table below and verify accuracy of the measured values. View the measured values on the relay in:

A2 Metering Data > Current Metering

5A Secondary

Injected Current 5A unit (A)	CT Primary	Expected Current Reading	Measured Current Phase A	Measured Current Phase B	Measured Current Phase C
0.5					
1.0					
2.5					
5.0					
7.5					
10.0					

1A Secondary

Injected Current 1A unit (A)	CT Primary	Expected Current Reading	Measured Current Phase A	Measured Current Phase B	Measured Current Phase C
0.1					
0.2					
0.5					
1.0					
1.5					
2.0					

Voltage Input Accuracy Test

The 339 specification for voltage input accuracy is +/- 1% of range. Voltage Range 50 to 240 V. Perform the steps below to verify accuracy.

1. Determine the VT connection type from the relay settings file. (Wye or Delta)
2. Determine the voltage transformer ratio from the relay settings file.
3. Inject the values shown the table below and verify accuracy of the measured values. View the measure values on the relay in:

A2 Metering Data > Voltage Metering

wye connection

Applied Line-Neutral Voltage (V)	Expected Voltage Reading	Measured Voltage A-N	Measured Voltage B-N	Measured Voltage C-N
50				
100				
150				
200				
240				

delta connection

Applied Line-Line Voltage (V)	Expected Voltage Reading	Measured Voltage A-B	Measured Voltage B-C	Measured Voltage C-A
50				
100				
150				
200				
240				

Ground Accuracy Test

The 339 specification for 1 A/5 A ground current input accuracy is ±1% of reading at 1× CT, ±3% of reading from 0.2 to 20 × CT, ±20% of reading from 0.05 to 0.19 × CT.

5 A Input

1. Determine the Ground CT Primary amperage from the relay settings file.
2. Inject the values shown in the table below and verify accuracy of the measured values. View the measured values on the relay in:

A2 Metering Data > Current Metering

Injected Current 5 A unit (A)	CT Primary	Expected Current Reading	Measured Ground Current
0.5			
1.0			
2.5			
5.0			

1 A Input

1. Determine the Ground CT Primary amperage from the relay settings file.
2. Inject the values shown the table below and verify accuracy of the measured values. View the measure values on the relay in:

A2 Metering Data > Current Metering

Injected Current 1 A unit (A)	CT Primary	Expected Current Reading	Measured Ground Current
0.1			
0.2			
0.5			
1.0			

GE Multilin 50:0.025 Ground Accuracy Test

The 339 specification for GE Multilin 50:0.025 ground current input accuracy is +/- .1A and +/-.2A. Perform the steps below to verify accuracy.

50:0.025 Input

1. Verify that the Ground CT is set to 50:0.025. If not, then this test should not be performed.
2. Inject the values shown in the table below as primary values into a GE Multilin 50:0.025 Core Balance CT. Verify accuracy of the measured values. View the measured values in:

A2 Metering Data > Current Metering

Primary Injected Current (A)	Expected Current Reading (A)	Measured Ground Current (A)
0.25	0.25	
1.0	1.00	
10.0	10.00	

RTD Accuracy Test

The 339 specification for RTD input accuracy is +/- 2°C. Perform the steps below.

1. Determine the RTD #1 Application type from the relay settings files..
2. Verify the RTD #1 Application setpoint has been programmed.
3. Measured values should be +/-2°C. Aapply resistance to the RTD inputs as per the table below to simulate RTDs and verify accuracy of the measured values. View the measured values on the relay in:

A2 Metering Data > Temperature

Repeat these steps for RTDs #2 to #12.

Applied Resistance 100 Ω Platinum	Expected RTD Temperature Reading	Measured RTD Temperature Select One: _____ °C											
	° Celsius	1	2	3	4	5	6	7	8	9	10	11	12
80.31	-50												
100.00	0												
119.39	50												
138.50	100												
157.32	150												
175.84	200												
194.08	250												

Digital Inputs

The inputs can be verified easily with an external DC voltage supply. Perform the steps below to verify functionality of the hardware inputs. Ensure the relay is isolated from the system when performing these tests.

Actual Values > A1 Status > Contact Input

Contact #	Expected Status (Switch Open)	Pass / Fail	Expected Status (Switch Closed)	Pass/Fail
1	Open		Shorted	
2	Open		Shorted	
3	Open		Shorted	
4	Open		Shorted	
5	Open		Shorted	
6	Open		Shorted	
7	Open		Shorted	
8	Open		Shorted	
9	Open		Shorted	
10	Open		Shorted	

1. Program contact input threshold to 17 VDC
2. View the status of the hardware inputs
3. Contect DC Supply - to input common
4. Contect DC Supply + to input #1-10
5. View the status of the hardware input

Multilin 345

Transformer Protection

Maintenance Guide

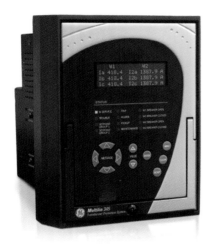

345 Maintenance Guide

Prior to maintenance on a relay, one should check if any service bulletins or product advisories exist for the relays in questions. This information can be found on the GE Multilin website or automatically downloaded from the EnerVista™ Launchpad document library.

If service bulletins or product advisories exist, the recommended remedial action should be implemented. Contact GE Multilin if any questions exist.

www.GEMultilin.com. 1-800-547-8629.

Recommended Tests

In-service maintenance:

1. Visual verification of analog value integrity such as voltage and current. Comparing metered values of the device with that of a corresponding system or device.
2. Visual verification of active alarms, relay display messages, self-test alarm messages, and LED indications.
3. Visual inspection on relay physical condition, noting any damage, corrosion, excessive dust, or loose wires.
4. Event recorder file download with further events analysis to compare and verify recorded data corresponds with other independently verified event information.
5. Download relay settings file and check against the settings on record.

Out-of-service maintenance:

Prior to taking the relay out-of-service, it is recommended to perform the following In-service test:

1. Visual verification of active alarms, relay display messages, self-test alarm messages, and LED indications.
2. Visual inspection on relay physical condition, noting any damage, corrosion, excessive dust, or loose wires.
3. Event recorder file download with further events analysis to compare and verify recorded data corresponds with other independently verified event information.

For the following tests, the relay should be taken out-of-service.

1. Physically check wiring connections for integrity and inspect for damage.
2. Analog values injection test (currents, voltages) and metering accuracy verification. Tests the following hardware: CT inputs, ground inputs, low pass filters, sample and hold buffers, zero-crossing circuitry and multiplexer. Calibrated test equipment is required.
3. Test each relay communication port using the 345 Setup program and verify functionality of USB, RS485, and if applicable Ethernet transceivers.
4. Setting change history using Viewpoint Maintenance software.
5. As-is settings comparison with as-left setting files using the 345 Setup software.

6. Secondary injection testing of AC quantities, DC signals to verify correct measurements are displayed.

7. Contact inputs and outputs verification. This test can be conducted by direct change of state forcing or as part of the system functional testing.

8. Keypad test to verify that each key responds to key press.

9. 20 second control power removal to test Super-cap / backup by verifying relay date and time match before and after loss of power.

If these routine tests show that any element of the relay is defective, we recommend that GE Multilin be contacted to discuss the issue and make recommendations. Depending on the nature of the failure, it is not always necessary to remove the relay from service.

Unscheduled maintenance:

There are several events that may result in unscheduled maintenance being required on a protective relay, including:

• Relay self-test errors or spontaneous hardware failure.

• Unexpected protection operation for an external fault that otherwise should not have resulted in tripping.

• Failure of protection to trip for an external fault that resulted in the operation of an upstream protection to clear the fault.

In all cases where there is a relay failure or inappropriate relay response, GE Multilin CST (Customer Service Team) should be contacted for technical support, including relay repair and detailed event analysis.

Self-Test Message Evaluation

Routine maintenance on the 345 should begin with an evaluation of any Diagnostic Messages of the relay either through the front panel, or remotely through the EnerVista™ Software program. The 345 relays perform self-test diagnostics at initialization and continuously as a background task. This ensures every testable component of the hardware and software is functioning correctly. There are two types of warnings displayed when the self-test detects a problem:

Major Problem: a serious problem that compromises all aspects of relay operation.

Minor Problem: a problem with the relay that does not compromise protection.

Diagnostic messages are automatically displayed for any active conditions in the relay such as trips, alarms, or asserted logic elements. These messages provide a summary of the present state of the relay.

Minor Self-test Errors

Self-test Error Message	Latched Target Message?	Description of Problem	How Often the Test is Performed	What to do
MAINTENANCE ALERT: IRIG-B Failure	No	A bad IRIG-B input signal has been detected.	Every 5 seconds*	Ensure IRIG-B cable is connected, check cable functionality (i.e. physical damage or perform continuity test), ensure IRIG-B receiver is functioning, and check input signal level (it may be less than specification). If none of these apply, contact the factory.
MAINTENANCE ALERT: Clock Not Set	No	Clock time is the same as the default time.	Every 5 seconds*	Set the date and time in PRODUCT SETUP.
MAINTENANCE ALERT: Comm Alert 1, 2, or 3	No	Communication error between CPU and Comms board.	Every 5 seconds*	If alert doesn't self-reset, then contact factory. Otherwise monitor reccurences as errors are detected and self-reset.
MAINTENANCE ALERT : Ethernet Link Fail	No	Communication error between 350 and Network.	Detected Instantaneously	Check Ethernet cable and Ethernet connection. Check health of the network. Check status of external routers and switches.

Major Self-test Errors

Self-test Error Message	Latched Target Message?	Description of Problem	How Often the Test is Performed	What to do
UNIT FAILURE: Contact Factory (XXXX)	Yes	This warning is caused by a unit hardware failure. Failure code (XXXX) is shown.	Every 5 seconds*	Contact the factory and provide the failure code.
RELAY NOT READY: Check Settings	No	PRODUCT SETUP INSTALLATION setting indicates that relay is not in a programmed state.	On power up and whenever the PRODUCT SETUP INSTALLATION setting is altered.	Program all required settings then set the PRODUCT SETUP INSTALLATION setting to "Ready".

* Failure is logged after the detection of 5 consecutive failures - that is, after 25 seconds.

345 Maintenance Worksheet

Hardware Functional Tests

Device Summary	
Device Name:	
Device Type:	
Order Code:	
Firmware Version:	
Serial Number:	
IP Address:	
Modbus Slave Address:	

Settings Summary	
Setting File Name:	
Last Changed:	
Changed by Whom (MAC Address)	

Do not change relay settings in order to perform maintenance testing on relays that have been commissioned.

Download the relay settings file and have these values available to conduct the following functional tests.

Phase Current Accuracy Test

The 345 specification for phase current accuracy is ±1% of reading at 1× CT, ±3% of reading from 0.2 to 20 × CT, ±20% of reading from 0.05 to 0.19 × CT. Perform the steps below to verify accuracy.

1. Determine the Phase CT Primary amperage from the relay settings file for each winding.

2. Inject the values shown in the table below and verify accuracy of the measured values for each winding connected. View the measured values on the relay in:

Actual Values > A2 Metering > Current > Winding Currents

5A Secondary

Injected Current 5A unit (A)	CT Primary	Winding 1				Winding 2			
		Expected Current Reading	Measured Current Phase A	Measured Current Phase B	Measured Current Phase C	Expected Current Reading	Measured Current Phase A	Measured Current Phase B	Measured Current Phase C
0.5									
1.0									
2.5									
5.0									
7.5									
10.0									

1A Secondary

Injected Current 1A unit (A)	CT Primary	Winding 1				Winding 2			
		Expected Current Reading	Measured Current Phase A	Measured Current Phase B	Measured Current Phase C	Expected Current Reading	Measured Current Phase A	Measured Current Phase B	Measured Current Phase C
0.1									
0.2									
0.5									
1.0									
1.5									
2.0									

Ground (5 A or 1 A) Current Accuracy Test

The 345 specification for ground current input accuracy is ±1% of reading at 1× CT, ±3% of reading from 0.2 to 20 × CT, ±20% of reading from 0.05 to 0.19 × CT. Perform the steps below to verify accuracy.

5 A Input

1. Determine the Ground CT Primary amperage from the relay settings file for each winding.

2. Inject the values shown in the table below and verify accuracy of the measured values. View the measured values on the relay in:

A2 Metering Data > Current Metering

5 A Secondary

Injected Current 5 A unit (A)	Winding 1				Winding 2		
	CT Primary	Expected Current Reading	Measured Ground Current	CT Primary	Expected Current Reading	Measured Ground Current	
0.5							
1.0							
2.5							
5.0							
7.5							
10.0							

1 A Secondary

Injected Current 1 A unit (A)	Winding 1				Winding 2		
	CT Primary	Expected Current Reading	Measured Ground Current	CT Primary	Expected Current Reading	Measured Ground Current	
0.5							
1.0							
2.5							
5.0							
7.5							
10.0							

Digital Inputs

The inputs can be verified easily with an external DC voltage supply. Perform the steps below to verify functionality of the hardware inputs. Ensure the relay is isolated from the system when performing these tests.

Actual Values > A1 Status > Contact Input

Contact #	Expected Status (Switch Open)	Pass / Fail	Expected Status (Switch Closed)	Pass/Fail
1	Open		Shorted	
2	Open		Shorted	
3	Open		Shorted	
4	Open		Shorted	
5	Open		Shorted	
6	Open		Shorted	
7	Open		Shorted	
8	Open		Shorted	
9	Open		Shorted	
10	Open		Shorted	

1. Program contact input threshold to 17 VDC
2. View the status of the hardware inputs
3. Contect DC Supply - to input common
4. Contect DC Supply + to input #1-10
5. View the status of the hardware input

Multilin 369

Motor Protection

Maintenance Guide

369 Maintenance Guide

Prior to maintenance on a relay, one should check if any service bulletins or product advisories exist for the relays in questions. This information can be found on the GE Multilin website or automatically downloaded from the EnerVista™ Launchpad document library.

If service bulletins or product advisories exist, the recommended remedial action should be implemented. Contact GE Multilin if any questions exist.

www.GEMultilin.com. 1-800-547-8629.

Recommended Tests

In-service maintenance:

1. Visual verification of analog value integrity such as voltage and current. Comparing metered values of the device with that of a corresponding system or device.
2. Visual verification of active alarms, relay display messages, self-test alarm messages, and LED indications.
3. LED test.
4. Visual inspection on relay physical condition, noting any damage, corrosion, excessive dust, or loose wires.
5. Event recorder file download with further events analysis to compare and verify recorded data corresponds with other independently verified event information.
6. Download relay settings file and check against the settings on record.

Out-of-service maintenance:

Prior to taking the relay out-of-service, it is recommended to perform the following In-service test:

1. Visual verification of active alarms, relay display messages, self-test alarm messages, and LED indications.
2. Visual inspection on relay physical condition, noting any damage, corrosion, excessive dust, or loose wires.
3. Event recorder file download with further events analysis to compare and verify recorded data corresponds with other independently verified event information.

For the following tests, the relay should be taken out-of-service.

1. Physically check wiring connections for integrity and inspect relay guide clips, shorting clips for wear and damage.
2. Analog values injection test (currents, voltages, RTDs, analog inputs) and metering accuracy verification. Tests the following hardware: CT inputs, ground inputs, low pass filters, sample and hold buffers, zero-crossing circuitry and multiplexer. Calibrated test equipment is required.
3. Test each relay communication port using the 369 Setup program and verify functionality of RS232, RS485, and if applicable Ethernet transceivers.

4. Setting change history using Viewpoint Maintenance software.

5. As-is settings comparison with as-left setting files using the 369 Setup software.

6. Secondary injection testing of AC quantities, DC signals to verify correct measurements are displayed.

7. Contact inputs and outputs verification. This test can be conducted by direct change of state forcing or as part of the system functional testing. Test Trip/Close coil monitors, logic inputs, solid-state outputs, output relays, analog outputs, and D/A converter.

8. LED Test and pushbutton continuity check.

9. Keypad test to verify that each key responds to key press.

10. 20 second control power removal to test Super-cap / battery backup by verifying relay date and time match before and after loss of power.

If these routine tests show that any element of the relay is defective, we recommend that GE Multilin be contacted to discuss the issue and make recommendations. Depending on the nature of the failure, it is not always necessary to remove the relay from service.

Unscheduled maintenance:

There are several events that may result in unscheduled maintenance being required on a protective relay, including:

- Relay self-test errors or spontaneous hardware failure.

- Unexpected protection operation for an external fault that otherwise should not have resulted in tripping.

- Failure of protection to trip for an internal fault that resulted in the operation of an upstream protection to clear the fault.

In all cases where there is a relay failure or inappropriate relay response, GE Multilin CST (Customer Service Team) should be contacted for technical support, including relay repair and detailed event analysis.

Self-Test Message Evaluation

Routine maintenance on the 369 should begin with an evaluation of any Diagnostic Messages of the relay either through the front panel, or remotely through the EnerVista™ Software program. The 369 relays perform self-test diagnostics at initialization and continuously as a background task. This ensures every testable component of the hardware and software is functioning correctly.

Diagnostic messages are automatically displayed for any active conditions in the relay such as trips, alarms, or asserted logic inputs. These messages provide a summary of the present state of the relay.

The 369 Relay performs self-diagnostics of the hardware circuitry. In the event that the device fails an internal self-test, the SERVICE LED indicates the failure. A relay must be assigned to the self-testing feature. This can be done in the device menu through:

S2 System Setup > Monitoring Setup > Self Test Mode

The relay programmed as the Self-Test relay activates upon a failure of any self-diagnostic test.

Additionally, an event is triggered in the event record when a self-test failure occurs.

LED indicators	
TRIP	Trip relay has operated (energized).
ALARM	Alarm relay has operated (energized).
AUX 1	Auxiliary relay has operated (energized).
AUX 2	Auxiliary relay has operated (energized).
SERVICE	Relay in need of technical service.
STOPPED	The protected motor is stopped.
STARTING	The protected motor is starting.
RUNNING	The protected motor is running.
OVERLOAD	The protected motor is in overload.
LOCKOUT	The motor is locked out.

369 Maintenance Worksheet

Hardware Functional Tests

Device Summary	
Device Name:	
Device Type:	
Order Code:	
Firmware Version:	
Serial Number:	
IP Address:	
Modbus Slave Address:	

Settings Summary	
Setting File Name:	
Last Changed:	
Changed by Whom (MAC Address)	

Do not change relay setting in order to perform maintenance testing on relays that have been commissioned.

Download the relay settings file and have these values available to conduct the following functional tests.

Phase Current Accuracy Test

Routine maintenance on the 369 should begin with an evaluation of the Diagnostic Messages of the relay either through the front panel, or remotely through the EnerVista™ software program. The 369 relays perform self-test diagnostics at initialization and continuously as a background task. This ensures every testable component of the hardware and software is functioning correctly.

1. Determine the Phase CT Primary amperage from the relay settings file.

2. Inject the values shown the table below and verify accuracy of the measured values. View the measure values on the relay in:

A2 Metering Data > Current Metering

Additionally, an event is triggered in the event record when a self-test failure occurs.

5A Secondary

Injected Current 5A unit (A)	CT Primary	Expected Current Reading	Measured Current Phase A	Measured Current Phase B	Measured Current Phase C
0.5					
1.0					
2.5					
5.0					
7.5					
10.0					

1A Secondary

Injected Current 1A unit (A)	CT Primary	Expected Current Reading	Measured Current Phase A	Measured Current Phase B	Measured Current Phase C
0.1					
0.2					
0.5					
1.0					
1.5					
2.0					

Voltage Input Accuracy Test

The 369 specification for voltage input accuracy is +/- 1.0% of full scale (240 V). Perform the steps below to verify accuracy.

1. Determine the VT connection type from the relay settings file. (Wye or Delta)
2. Determine the voltage transformer ratio from the relay settings file.
3. Inject the values shown the table below and verify accuracy of the measured values. View the measure values on the relay in:

A2 Metering Data > Voltage Metering

wye connection

Applied Line-Neutral Voltage (V)	Expected Voltage Reading	Measured Voltage A-N	Measured Voltage B-N	Measured Voltage C-N
30				
50				
100				
150				
200				
270				

delta connection

Applied Line-Neutral Voltage (V)	Expected Voltage Reading	Measured Voltage A-B	Measured Voltage B-C	Measured Voltage C-A
30				
50				
100				
150				
200				
270				

Ground (5A or 1A) Accuracy Test

The 369 specification for the 1 A/5 A ground current input accuracy is +/- 0.5% of 1 × CT for the 5A and 0.5% of 5 × CT for the 1 A input.

5 A Input

1. Determine the Ground CT Primary amperage from the relay settings file.
2. Measured values should be +/-5 A. Inject the values shown the table below and verify accuracy of the measured values. View the measure values on the relay in:

A2 Metering Data > Current Metering

Injected Current 5A unit (A)	CT Primary	Expected Current Reading	Measured Ground Current
0.5			
1.0			
2.5			
5.0			

1 A Input

1. Determine the Ground CT Primary amperage from the relay settings file.
2. Measured values should be +/-2.5 A. Inject the values shown the table below and verify accuracy of the measured values. View the measure values on the relay in:

A2 Metering Data > Current Metering

Injected Current 5A unit (A)	CT Primary	Expected Current Reading	Measured Ground Current
0.1			
0.2			
0.5			
1.0			

GE Multilin 50:0.025 Ground Accuracy Test

The 369 specification for GE Multilin 50:0.025 ground current input accuracy is +/- 0.5% of CT rate primary (25A). Perform the steps below to verify accuracy.

5 A Input

1. Verify that the Ground CT is set to 50:0.025. If not, then this test should not be performed.
2. Measured values should be +/-0.125 A. Inject the values shown the table below either as primary values into a GE Multilin 50:0.025 Core Balance CT or as secondary values that simulate the core balance CT. Verify accuracy of the measure values. View the measured values in:

A2 Metering Data > Current Metering

Primary Injected Current (A)	Secondary Injected Current (mA)	Expected Current Reading (A)	Measured Ground Current (A)
0.25	0.125	0.25	
1.0	0.5	1.00	
10.0	5.0	10.00	
25.0	12.5	25.00	

RTD Accuracy Test

The 369 specification for RTD input accuracy is +/- 2°C. Perform the steps below.

1. Determine the Stator RTD Type from the relay settings file.
2. Determine the RTD #1 Application type from the relay settings files.
3. Measured values should be +/-2°C or +/-4°F. After resistances applied to the RTD inputs as per the table below to simulate RTDs and verify accuracy of the measured values. View the measure values on the relay in:

A2 Metering Data > Temperature

Repeat these steps for RTDs #2 to #12.

Applied Resistance 100 Ω Platinum	Expected RTD Temperature Reading		Measured RTD Temperature Select One: _____ °C _____ °F											
	° Celsius	° Fahrenheit	1	2	3	4	5	6	7	8	9	10	11	12
84.27	-40	-40												
100.00	0	32												
119.39	50	122												
138.50	100	212												
157.32	150	302												
175.84	200	392												

Applied Resistance 120 Ω Nickel	Expected RTD Temperature Reading		Measured RTD Temperature Select One: _____ °C _____ °F											
	° Celsius	° Fahrenheit	1	2	3	4	5	6	7	8	9	10	11	12
92.76	-40	-40												
120.00	0	32												
157.74	50	122												
200.64	100	212												
248.95	150	302												
303.46	200	392												

Applied Resistance 100 Ω Nickel	Expected RTD Temperature Reading		Measured RTD Temperature Select One: _____ °C _____ °F											
	° Celsius	° Fahrenheit	1	2	3	4	5	6	7	8	9	10	11	12
77.30	-40	-40												
100.00	0	32												
131.45	50	122												
167.2	100	212												
207.45	150	302												
252.88	200	392												

Applied Resistance 10 Ω Copper	Expected RTD Temperature Reading		Measured RTD Temperature Select One: _____ °C _____ °F											
	° Celsius	° Fahrenheit	1	2	3	4	5	6	7	8	9	10	11	12
7.49	-40	-40												
9.04	0	32												
10.97	50	122												
12.9	100	212												
14.83	150	302												
16.78	200	392												

Digital Inputs

The digital inputs can be verified easily with a simple switch or pushbutton. Perform the steps below to verify functionality of the digital inputs. Ensure the relay is isolated from the system when performing these tests.

1. Open switches of all of the digital inputs.
2. View the status of the digital inputs in:

Actual Values > A1 Status > Digital Inputs

3. Close switches of all of the digital inputs.
4. View the status of the digital inputs in:

Actual Values > A1 Status > Digital Inputs

Input	Expected Status (Switch Open)	Pass / Fail	Expected Status (Switch Closed)	Pass/Fail
Spare	Open		Shorted	
Differential Relay	Open		Shorted	
Speed Switch	Open		Shorted	
Access Switch	Open		Shorted	
Emergency Restart	Open		Shorted	
External Reset	Open		Shorted	

Analog Inputs and Outputs

The 369 specification for analog input and analog output accuracy is +/-1% of full scale. Perform the steps below to verify accuracy. Determine from the relay settings file whether analog input is a 4 to 20 mA, 0 to 20mA, or 0 to 1 mA, and use the appropriate test table. Repeat these tests for analog outputs 2 to 4.

4 to 20mA Analog Input – Start with Analog Input #1

1. Determine the type, Analog Input1 Minimum, and Analog Input1 Maximum from the relay settings file.

2. Analog output values should be +/- 0.2 mA on the ammeter. Measured analog input values should be +/- 10 units. Force the analog outputs using the following setpoints:

S11 Testing > Test Analog Output > Force Analog Output 1: "0%"

(Enter each desired force value in percent; repeat for Analog Outputs 2 through 4)

3. Verify the ammeter readings as well as the measured analog input readings. For the purposes of testing, the analog input is fed in from the analog output. View the measured values in:

A2 Metering Data > Analog Inputs

Analog Output Force Value (%)	Expected Ammeter Reading (mA)	Measured Ammeter Reading (mA)				Expected Analog Input Reading	Measure Analog Input Reading (units)			
		1	2	3	4		1	2	3	4
0%	4									
25%	8									
50%	12									
75%	16									
100%	20									

0 to 1mA Analog Input – Start with Analog Input #1

1. Determine the type, Analog Input1 Minimum, and Analog Input1 Maximum from the relay settings file.
2. Analog output values should be +/- 0.01 mA on the ammeter. Measured analog input values should be +/- 10 units. Force the analog outputs using the following setpoints:

S11 Testing > Test Analog Outputs > Force Analog Output 1: "0%"

(Enter each desired force value in percent; repeat for Analog Outputs 2 through 4)

3. Verify the ammeter readings as well as the measured analog input readings. For the purposes of testing, the analog input is fed in from the analog output. View the measured values in:

A2 Metering Data > Analog Inputs

Analog Output Force Value (%)	Expected Ammeter Reading (mA)	Measured Ammeter Reading (mA)				Expected Analog Input Reading	Measure Analog Input Reading (units)			
		1	2	3	4		1	2	3	4
0%	0									
25%	0.25									
50%	0.50									
75%	0.75									
100%	1.00									

0 to 20mA Analog Input – Start with Analog Input #1

1. Determine the type, Analog Input1 Minimum, and Analog Input1 Maximum from the relay settings file.

2. Analog output values should be +/- 0.2 mA on the ammeter. Measured analog input values should be +/- 10 units. Force the analog outputs using the following setpoints:

S11 Testing > Test Analog Output > Force Analog Output 1: "0%"

(Enter each desired force value in percent; repeat for Analog Outputs 2 through 4)

3. Verify the ammeter readings as well as the measured analog input readings. For the purposes of testing, the analog input is fed in from the analog output. View the measured values in:

A2 Metering Data > Analog Inputs

Analog Output Force Value (%)	Expected Ammeter Reading (mA)	Measured Ammeter Reading (mA)				Expected Analog Input Reading	Measure Analog Input Reading (units)			
		1	2	3	4		1	2	3	4
0%	0									
25%	5									
50%	10									
75%	15									
100%	20									

Output Relays

Ensure the relay is isolated from the system when performing these tests.

To verify the functionality of the output relays, perform the following steps:

1. Using the setpoint:

> **S11 Testing > Test Output Relays > Force Trip Relay: "Energized"**
>
> **S11 Testing > Test Output Relays > Force Trip Relay Duration: "Static"**

2. Using the above setpoints, individually select each of the other output relays (AUX 1, AUX 2, and ALARM) and verify operation.

Force Operation Setpoint	Expected Measurement Check For Short								Actual Measurement Check for Short							
	R1		R2		R3		R4		R1		R2		R3		R4	
	NO	NC	NO	NC	NO	NC	NO	NC	NO	NC	NO	NC	NO	NC	NO	NC
R1 Trip	X			X	X			X								
R2 Auxiliary		X	X		X			X								
R3 Auxiliary		X		X	X			X								
R4 Alarm		X		X		X	X									

Multilin 269PLUS
Motor Protection

Maintenance Guide

269Plus Maintenance Guide

Prior to maintenance on a relay, one should check if any service bulletins or product advisories exist for the relays in questions. This information can be found on the GE Multilin website or automatically downloaded from the EnerVista™ Launchpad document library.

If service bulletins or product advisories exist, the recommended remedial action should be implemented. Contact GE Multilin if any questions exist.

www.GEMultilin.com. 1-800-547-8629.

Recommended Tests

In-service maintenance:

1. Visual verification of analog value integrity such as voltage and current. Comparing metered values of the device with that of a corresponding system or device.
2. Visual verification of active alarms, relay display messages, self-test alarm messages, and LED indications.
3. LED test.
4. Visual inspection on relay physical condition, noting any damage, corrosion, excessive dust, or loose wires.
5. Event recorder file download with further events analysis to compare and verify recorded data corresponds with other independently verified event information.
6. Download relay settings file and check against the settings on record.

Out-of-service maintenance:

Prior to taking the relay out-of-service, it is recommended to perform the following In-service test:

1. Visual verification of active alarms, relay display messages, self-test alarm messages, and LED indications.
2. Visual inspection on relay physical condition, noting any damage, corrosion, excessive dust, or loose wires.
3. Event recorder file download with further events analysis to compare and verify recorded data corresponds with other independently verified event information.

For the following tests, the relay should be taken out-of-service.

1. Physically check wiring connections for integrity and inspect relay guide clips, shorting clips for wear and damage.
2. Analog values injection test (currents, voltages, RTDs, analog inputs) and metering accuracy verification. Tests the following hardware: CT inputs, ground inputs, low pass filters, sample and hold buffers, zero-crossing circuitry and multiplexer. Calibrated test equipment is required.
3. Test each relay communication port using the 269Plus Setup program and verify functionality of RS232 transceiver and RS485 transceiver.

4. Setting change history using Viewpoint Maintenance software.

5. As-is settings comparison with as-left setting files using the 269Plus Setup software.

6. Secondary injection testing of AC quantities, DC signals to verify correct measurements are displayed.

7. Contact inputs and outputs verification. This test can be conducted by direct change of state forcing or as part of the system functional testing. Test Trip/Close coil monitors, logic inputs, solid-state outputs, output relays, analog outputs, and D/A converter.

8. LED Test and pushbutton continuity check.

9. 20 second control power removal to test Super-cap / battery backup by verifying relay date and time match before and after loss of power.

If these routine tests show that any element of the relay is defective, we recommend that GE Multilin be contacted to discuss the issue and make recommendations. Depending on the nature of the failure, it is not always necessary to remove the relay from service.

Unscheduled maintenance:

There are several events that may result in unscheduled maintenance being required on a protective relay, including:

- Relay self-test errors or spontaneous hardware failure.

- Unexpected protection operation for an external fault that otherwise should not have resulted in tripping.

- Failure of protection to trip for an internal fault that resulted in the operation of an upstream protection to clear the fault.

In all cases where there is a relay failure or inappropriate relay response, GE Multilin CST (Customer Service Team) should be contacted for technical support, including relay repair and detailed event analysis.

Self-Test Message Evaluation

Routine maintenance on the 269Plus should begin with an evaluation of any Diagnostic Messages of the relay either through the front panel, or remotely through the EnerVista™ Software program. The 269Plus relays perform self-test diagnostics at initialization and continuously as a background task. This ensures every testable component of the hardware and software is functioning correctly.

Diagnostic messages are automatically displayed for any active conditions in the relay such as trips, alarms, or asserted logic inputs. These messages provide a summary of the present state of the relay. The SERVICE LED flashes when there are diagnostic messages present. The output relay programmed for the self-test feature will activate, and display will show one of the specific self-test alarm messages from the table below.

Self Test Message	Component / Function Affected	Severity	Failure Description
Self-Test Alarm A/D H/W Fail	A/D Converter	Major	Caused by a failure of the analog to digital converter. The integrity of system essential input measurements is affected by this failure. All metering and protective functions will be suspended. Return relay for service.
Self-Test Alarm RTD H/W Fail, RTDs Off	RTD Circuit	Major	Caused by a failure of the RTD circuitry. # OF STATOR RTDs USED setpoint automatically set to 0. RTD ALARM and TRIP automatically set to OFF. Current-related functions will continue normal operation. Return relay for service.
Self-Test Alarm RAM Fail	RAM Corruption (Memory/Stored Data)	Major	Caused by a failure in the relay RAM that has been detected, which cannot be self-corrected. Every relay function is at risk of malfunctioning due to this memory error. Return relay for service.
Self-Test Alarm Factory Setpoints Loaded	NOVRAM Corruption (Memory/Stored Data)	Major	Caused by a failure in the relay NOVRAM that has been detected, which cannot be self-corrected. Every relay function is at risk of malfunctioning due to this memory error. Return relay for service.

269Plus Maintenance Worksheet

Hardware Functional Tests

Device Summary	
Device Name:	
Device Type:	
Order Code:	
Firmware Version:	
Serial Number:	
IP Address:	
Modbus Slave Address:	

Settings Summary	
Setting File Name:	
Last Changed:	
Changed by Whom (MAC Address)	

Do not change relay setting in order to perform maintenance testing on relays that have been commissioned.

Download the relay settings file and have these values available to conduct the following functional tests.

Phase Current Accuracy Test

The 269Plus specification for phase current accuracy is +/- 0.5% of 2 x CT when the injected current is less than 2 x CT. Perform the steps below to verify accuracy.

1. Determine the Phase CT Primary amperage from the relay settings file.
2. Inject the values shown the table below and verify accuracy of the measured values. View the measure values on the relay in:

Actual Values > Phase Current Data

5A Secondary

Injected Current 5A unit (A)	CT Primary	Expected Current Reading	Measured Current Phase A	Measured Current Phase B	Measured Current Phase C
0.5					
1.0					
2.5					
5.0					
7.5					
10.0					

1A Secondary

Injected Current 1A unit (A)	CT Primary	Expected Current Reading	Measured Current Phase A	Measured Current Phase B	Measured Current Phase C
0.1					
0.2					
0.5					
1.0					
1.5					
2.0					

Voltage Input Accuracy Test

The 269Plus specification for voltage input accuracy is +/- 0.5% of full scale (200 V AC). Perform the steps below to verify accuracy.

1. Determine the VT connection type from the relay settings file. (Wye or Delta)
2. Determine the voltage transformer ratio from the relay settings file.
3. Inject the values shown the table below and verify accuracy of the measured values. View the measure values on the relay in:

Actual Values > Metering Data

wye connection

Applied Line-Neutral Voltage (V)	Expected Voltage Reading	Measured Voltage A-N	Measured Voltage B-N	Measured Voltage C-N
30				
50				
100				
150				
200				

delta connection

Applied Line-Neutral Voltage (V)	Expected Voltage Reading	Measured Voltage A-B	Measured Voltage B-C	Measured Voltage C-A
30				
50				
100				
150				
200				

Ground (5A or 1A) Accuracy Test

The 269Plus specification for ground current input accuracy is +/- 4% of ground fault CT primary amps setpoint.

5 A Input

1. Determine the Ground CT Primary amperage from the relay settings file.
2. Inject the values shown the table below and verify accuracy of the measured values. View the measure values on the relay in:

Actual Values > Ground Fault Current

Injected Current 5A unit (A)	CT Primary	Expected Current Reading	Measured Ground Current
0.5			
1.0			
2.5			
5.0			

1 A Input

1. Determine the Ground CT Primary amperage from the relay settings file.
2. Inject the values shown the table below and verify accuracy of the measured values. View the measure values on the relay in:

Actual Values > Ground Fault Current

Injected Current 5A unit (A)	CT Primary	Expected Current Reading	Measured Ground Current
0.1			
0.2			
0.5			
1.0			

RTD Accuracy Test

The 269Plus specification for RTD input accuracy is +/- 2°C. Perform the steps below.

1. Determine the Stator RTD Type from the relay settings file.
2. Determine the RTD #1 Application type from the relay settings files.
3. Measured values should be +/-2°C or +/-4°F. After resistances applied to the RTD inputs as per the table below to simulate RTDs and verify accuracy of the measured values. View the measure values on the relay in:

Actual Values > RTD Temperature Data

Repeat these steps for RTDs #2 to #10.

Applied Resistance 100 Ω Platinum	Expected RTD Temperature Reading		Measured RTD Temperature Select One: _____ °C _____ °F									
	° Celsius	° Fahrenheit	1	2	3	4	5	6	7	8	9	10
84.27	-40	-40										
100.00	0	32										
119.39	50	122										
138.50	100	212										
157.32	150	302										
175.84	200	392										

Applied Resistance 120 Ω Nickel	Expected RTD Temperature Reading		Measured RTD Temperature Select One: _____ °C _____ °F									
	° Celsius	° Fahrenheit	1	2	3	4	5	6	7	8	9	10
92.76	-40	-40										
120.00	0	32										
157.74	50	122										
200.64	100	212										
248.95	150	302										
303.46	200	392										

Applied Resistance 100 Ω Nickel	Expected RTD Temperature Reading		Measured RTD Temperature Select One: _____°C _____°F									
	° Celsius	° Fahrenheit	1	2	3	4	5	6	7	8	9	10
77.30	-40	-40										
100.00	0	32										
131.45	50	122										
167.2	100	212										
207.45	150	302										
252.88	200	392										

Applied Resistance 10 Ω Copper	Expected RTD Temperature Reading		Measured RTD Temperature Select One: _____°C _____°F									
	° Celsius	° Fahrenheit	1	2	3	4	5	6	7	8	9	10
7.49	-40	-40										
9.04	0	32										
10.97	50	122										
12.9	100	212										
14.83	150	302										
16.78	200	392										

Digital Inputs

The digital inputs can be verified easily with a simple switch or pushbutton. Perform the steps below to verify functionality of the digital inputs. Ensure the relay is isolated from the system when performing these tests.

1. Open switches of all of the digital inputs.
2. View the status of the digital inputs in:

Setpoints > GE Multilin Service Codes > Status (line 6)

3. Close switches of all of the digital inputs.
4. View the status of the digital inputs in:

Setpoints > GE Multilin Service Codes > Status (line 6)

Input	Expected Status (Switch Open)	Pass / Fail	Expected Status (Switch Closed)	Pass/Fail
Input	Open		Shorted	
Speed	Open		Shorted	
Differential	Open		Shorted	
Access	Open		Shorted	
Emergency Restart	Open		Shorted	
External	Open		Shorted	

Analog Inputs

The 269Plus specification for analog output accuracy is +/-1% of full scale. Perform the steps below to verify accuracy. Determine from the relay settings file whether analog output is 4 to 20 mA, 0 to 20mA, or 0 to 1 mA. Then use the appropriate test table.

4 to 20mA Analog Input – Start with Analog Input #1

1. Force the analog outputs using the following setpoints:

Setpoints > GE Multilin Service Codes > Analog Outputs Forced To:

(Enter desired value of Zero, Mid, or Full Scale)

2. Verify with an ammeter the output values.

Analog Output Force Value (%)	Expected Ammeter Reading 4 to 20mA (mA)	Expected Ammeter Reading 0 to 20mA (mA)	Expected Ammeter Reading 0 to 1mA (mA)	Measured Ammeter Reading (mA)
0%	4	0	0	
50%	12	10	0.50	
100%	20	20	1.00	

Output Relays

Output relays can be exercised in the 269Plus relay. However, based on the order code, the settings for the failsafe states of the contacts vary. Therefore, please refer to the 269Plus Instruction Manual for the output relay testing procedure.

Multilin MM300

Motor Protection

Maintenance Guide

MM300 Maintenance Guide

Prior to maintenance on a relay, one should check if any service bulletins or product advisories exist for the relays in questions. This information can be found on the GE Multilin website or automatically downloaded from the EnerVista™ Launchpad document library.

If service bulletins or product advisories exist, the recommended remedial action should be implemented. Contact GE Multilin if any questions exist.

www.GEMultilin.com. 1-800-547-8629.

Recommended Tests

In-service maintenance:

1. Visual verification of analog value integrity such as voltage and current. Comparing metered values of the device with that of a corresponding system or device.
2. Visual verification of active alarms, relay display messages, self-test alarm messages, and LED indications.
3. LED test.
4. Visual inspection on relay physical condition, noting any damage, corrosion, excessive dust, or loose wires.
5. Event recorder file download with further events analysis to compare and verify recorded data corresponds with other independently verified event information.
6. Download relay settings file and check against the settings on record.

Out-of-service maintenance:

Prior to taking the relay out-of-service, it is recommended to perform the following In-service test:

1. Visual verification of active alarms, relay display messages, self-test alarm messages, and LED indications.
2. Visual inspection on relay physical condition, noting any damage, corrosion, excessive dust, or loose wires.
3. Event recorder file download with further events analysis to compare and verify recorded data corresponds with other independently verified event information.

For the following tests, the relay should be taken out-of-service.

1. Analog values injection test   (currents, voltages, RTDs, analog inputs) and metering accuracy verification. Tests the following hardware: CT inputs, ground inputs, low pass filters, sample and hold buffers, zero-crossing circuitry and multiplexer. Calibrated test equipment is required.
2. Test each relay communication port using the MM300 Setup program and verify functionality of RS232 transceiver and RS485 transceiver.
3. Setting change history using Viewpoint Maintenance software.

4. As-is settings comparison with as-left setting files using the MM300 Setup software.

5. Secondary injection testing of AC quantities, DC signals to verify correct measurements are displayed.

6. Contact inputs and outputs verification. This test can be conducted by direct change of state forcing or as part of the system functional testing. Logic inputs, output relays, analog outputs, and D/A converter.

7. LED Test and pushbutton continuity check.

8. 20 second control power removal to test Super-cap / battery backup by verifying relay date and time match before and after loss of power.

If these routine tests show that any element of the relay is defective, we recommend that GE Multilin be contacted to discuss the issue and make recommendations. Depending on the nature of the failure, it is not always necessary to remove the relay from service.

Unscheduled maintenance:

There are several events that may result in unscheduled maintenance being required on a protective relay, including:

- Relay self-test errors or spontaneous hardware failure.

- Unexpected protection operation for an external fault that otherwise should not have resulted in tripping.

- Failure of protection to trip for an internal fault that resulted in the operation of an upstream protection to clear the fault.

In all cases where there is a relay failure or inappropriate relay response, GE Multilin CST (Customer Service Team) should be contacted for technical support, including relay repair and detailed event analysis.

Self-Test Message Evaluation

Routine maintenance on the MM300 should begin with an evaluation of any Alarm messages of the relay either through the front panel, or remotely through the EnerVista™ Software program. The MM300 relays perform self-checking diagnostics at initialization and continuously as a background task. This ensures every testable component of the hardware and software is functioning correctly.

Alarm messages are automatically displayed for any active conditions in the relay such as trips, alarms, or asserted logic inputs. These messages provide a summary of the present state of the relay.

The MM300 Relay performs self-checking of the hardware circuitry. In the event that the device fails an internal self-test, the ALARM or TRIP LED indicates the failure. The message SELF TEST TRIP/ALARM is posted on status page.

This is a Major error. The MM300 must be replaced or repaired.

An internal fault during self-checking will cause an alarm or trip. Since operation may be erratic depending on the fault condition, it may be desirable to trip the motor by setting this setpoint to ENABLE. The MM300 continues to run the motor with an internal fault present if set to DISABLE of alarm.

MM300 Maintenance Worksheet

Hardware Functional Tests

Device Summary	
Device Name:	
Device Type:	
Order Code:	
Firmware Version:	
Serial Number:	
IP Address:	
Modbus Slave Address:	

Settings Summary	
Setting File Name:	
Last Changed:	
Changed by Whom (MAC Address)	

> Do not change relay setting in order to perform maintenance testing on relays that have been commissioned.
>
> Download the relay settings file and have these values available to conduct the following functional tests.

Phase Current Accuracy Test

The MM300 specification for phase current accuracy is +/- 2% of primary phase CT primary amps setpoint or +/- 2% of reading, whichever is higher. Perform the steps below to verify accuracy.

1. Determine the Phase CT Primary amperage from the relay settings file.
2. Inject the values shown the table below and verify accuracy of the measured values. View the measure values on the relay in:

A1: Data > Motor Data

5A Secondary

Injected Current 5A unit (A)	CT Primary	Expected Current Reading	Measured Current Phase A	Measured Current Phase B	Measured Current Phase C
0.5					
1.0					
2.5					
5.0					
7.5					
10.0					

1A Secondary

Injected Current 1A unit (A)	CT Primary	Expected Current Reading	Measured Current Phase A	Measured Current Phase B	Measured Current Phase C
0.1					
0.2					
0.5					
1.0					
1.5					
2.0					

Voltage Input Accuracy Test

The MM300 specification for voltage input accuracy is +/- 2% of VT primary or +/- 2% of reading; whichever is greater. Perform the steps below to verify accuracy.

1. Determine the voltage transformer ratio from the relay settings file.
2. Inject the values shown the table below and verify accuracy of the measured values. View the measure values on the relay in:

A1: Data > Motor Data > VT Volta

Applied Line-Neutral Voltage (V)	Expected Voltage Reading	Measured Voltage
30		
50		
100		
150		
200		

Ground Accuracy Test

The MM300 specification for 5 A secondary, ground current input accuracy is +/- 2% of full scale.

5 A Input

1. Determine the Ground CT Primary amperage from the relay settings file.
2. Inject the values shown the table below and verify accuracy of the measured values. View the measure values on the relay in:

A1: Data > Motor Data > Ground Current

Injected Current 5A unit (A)	CT Primary	Expected Current Reading	Measured Ground Current
0.5			
1.0			
2.5			
5.0			

Digital Inputs

Open and close each switch input and note that display reflects the present status of the input terminals. The status is shown as either OPEN or CLOSED.

The digital inputs can be verified easily with a simple switch or pushbutton. Perform the steps below to verify functionality of the digital inputs. Ensure the relay is isolated from the system when performing these tests.

1. Open switches of all of the digital inputs.
2. To view the status of each input one at a time, go to:

A3 Inputs > Input Contact

3. Close switches of all of the digital inputs.
4. View the status of the digital inputs in:

A3 Inputs > Input Contact

Input	Expected Status (Switch Open)	Pass / Fail	Expected Status (Switch Closed)	Pass/Fail
Start A	Open		Shorted	
Start B	Open		Shorted	
Stop Input	Open		Shorted	
Contactor A N/O	Open		Shorted	
Contactor B N/O	Open		Shorted	
Local Isolator N/O	Open		Shorted	
Interlock 1	Open		Shorted	
Interlock 2	Open		Shorted	
Interlock 3	Open		Shorted	
Interlock 4	Open		Shorted	
Interlock 5	Open		Shorted	
Interlock 6	Open		Shorted	
Interlock 7	Open		Shorted	
Interlock 8	Open		Shorted	
Interlock 9	Open		Shorted	
Interlock 10	Open		Shorted	

Multilin MM2
Motor Protection

Maintenance Guide

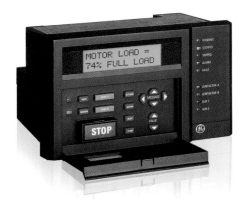

MM2 Maintenance Guide

Prior to maintenance on a relay, one should check if any service bulletins or product advisories exist for the relays in questions. This information can be found on the GE Multilin website or automatically downloaded from the EnerVista™ Launchpad document library.

If service bulletins or product advisories exist, the recommended remedial action should be implemented. Contact GE Multilin if any questions exist.

www.GEMultilin.com. 1-800-547-8629.

Recommended Tests

In-service maintenance:

1. Visual verification of analog value integrity such as voltage and current. Comparing metered values of the device with that of a corresponding system or device.
2. Visual verification of active alarms, relay display messages, self-test alarm messages, and LED indications.
3. LED test.
4. Visual inspection on relay physical condition, noting any damage, corrosion, excessive dust, or loose wires.
5. Download relay settings file and check against the settings on record.

Out-of-service maintenance:

Prior to taking the relay out-of-service, it is recommended to perform the following In-service test:

1. Visual verification of active alarms, relay display messages, self-test alarm messages, and LED indications.
2. Visual inspection on relay physical condition, noting any damage, corrosion, excessive dust, or loose wires.

For the following tests, the relay should be taken out-of-service.

1. Analog values injection test (currents, voltages, RTDs, analog inputs) and metering accuracy verification. Tests the following hardware: CT inputs, ground inputs, low pass filters, sample and hold buffers, zero-crossing circuitry and multiplexer. Calibrated test equipment is required.
2. Test each relay communication port using the MM2 Setup program and verify functionality of RS232 transceiver and RS485 transceiver.
3. Setting change history using Viewpoint Maintenance software.
4. As-is settings comparison with as-left setting files using the MM2 Setup software.
5. Secondary injection testing of AC quantities, DC signals to verify correct measurements are displayed.

6. Contact inputs and outputs verification. This test can be conducted by direct change of state forcing or as part of the system functional testing. Logic inputs, output relays, analog outputs, and D/A converter.

7. LED Test and pushbutton continuity check.

8. 20 second control power removal to test Super-cap / battery backup by verifying relay date and time match before and after loss of power.

If these routine tests show that any element of the relay is defective, we recommend that GE Multilin be contacted to discuss the issue and make recommendations. Depending on the nature of the failure, it is not always necessary to remove the relay from service.

Unscheduled maintenance:

There are several events that may result in unscheduled maintenance being required on a protective relay, including:

- Relay self-test errors or spontaneous hardware failure.
- Unexpected protection operation for an external fault that otherwise should not have resulted in tripping.
- Failure of protection to trip for an internal fault that resulted in the operation of an upstream protection to clear the fault.

In all cases where there is a relay failure or inappropriate relay response, GE Multilin CST (Customer Service Team) should be contacted for technical support, including relay repair and detailed event analysis.

Self-Test Message Evaluation

Routine maintenance on the MM2 should begin with an evaluation of any Alarm messages of the relay either through the front panel, or remotely through the EnerVista™ Software program. The MM2 relays perform self-checking diagnostics at initialization and continuously as a background task. This ensures every testable component of the hardware and software is functioning correctly.

Alarm messages are automatically displayed for any active conditions in the relay such as trips, alarms, or asserted logic inputs. These messages provide a summary of the present state of the relay.

The MM2 Relay performs self-checking of the hardware circuitry. In the event that the device fails an internal self-test, the FAULT LED indicates the failure. The message INTERNAL FAULT ALARM is shown on the display, indicating a internal hardware fault was detected.

This is a Major error. The MM2 must be replaced or repaired.

An internal fault during self-checking will cause an alarm. Since operation may be erratic depending on the fault condition, it may be desirable to trip the motor by setting this setpoint to ENABLE. The MM2 continues to run the motor with an internal fault present if set to DISABLE.

```
 ┌─────────────────────────────────────┐
 │   INTERNAL FAULT                     │
 │        ALARM                         │
 └─────────────────────────────────────┘
```

MM2 Maintenance Worksheet

Hardware Functional Tests

Device Summary	
Device Name:	
Device Type:	
Order Code:	
Firmware Version:	
Serial Number:	
IP Address:	
Modbus Slave Address:	

Settings Summary	
Setting File Name:	
Last Changed:	
Changed by Whom (MAC Address)	

Do not change relay setting in order to perform maintenance testing on relays that have been commissioned.

Download the relay settings file and have these values available to conduct the following functional tests.

Phase Current Accuracy Test

The MM2 specification for phase current accuracy is +/- 2% of primary phase CT primary amps setpoint or +/- 2% of reading, whichever is higher. Perform the steps below to verify accuracy.

1. Determine the Phase CT Primary amperage from the relay settings file.

2. Inject the values shown the table below and verify accuracy of the measured values. View the measure values on the relay in:

A1: Data > Motor Data

5A Secondary

Injected Current 5A unit (A)	CT Primary	Expected Current Reading	Measured Current Phase A	Measured Current Phase B	Measured Current Phase C
0.5					
1.0					
2.5					
5.0					
7.5					
10.0					

1A Secondary

Injected Current 1A unit (A)	CT Primary	Expected Current Reading	Measured Current Phase A	Measured Current Phase B	Measured Current Phase C
0.1					
0.2					
0.5					
1.0					
1.5					
2.0					

Voltage Input Accuracy Test

The MM2 specification for voltage input accuracy is +/- 2% of VT primary or +/- 2% of reading; whichever is greater. Perform the steps below to verify accuracy.

1. Determine the voltage transformer ratio from the relay settings file.
2. Inject the values shown the table below and verify accuracy of the measured values. View the measure values on the relay in:

A1: Data > Motor Data > VT Volta

Applied Line-Neutral Voltage (V)	Expected Voltage Reading	Measured Voltage
30		
50		
100		
150		
200		

Ground Accuracy Test

The MM2 specification for 5 A secondary, ground current input accuracy is +/- 2% of full scale.

5 A Input

1. Determine the Ground CT Primary amperage from the relay settings file.
2. Inject the values shown the table below and verify accuracy of the measured values. View the measure values on the relay in:

A1: Data > Motor Data > Ground Current

Injected Current 5A unit (A)	CT Primary	Expected Current Reading	Measured Ground Current
0.5			
1.0			
2.5			
5.0			

Digital Inputs

The MM2 specification for analog output accuracy is +/-1% of full scale. Open and close each switch input and note that display reflects the present status of the input terminals. The status is shown as either OPEN or CLOSED.

The digital inputs can be verified easily with a simple switch or pushbutton. Perform the steps below to verify functionality of the digital inputs. Ensure the relay is isolated from the system when performing these tests.

1. Open switches of all of the digital inputs.
2. To view the status of each input one at a time, go to:

A3 Inputs > Input Contact

3. Close switches of all of the digital inputs.
4. View the status of the digital inputs in:

A3 Inputs > Input Contact

Input	Expected Status (Switch Open)	Pass / Fail	Expected Status (Switch Closed)	Pass/Fail
Start A	Open		Shorted	
Start B	Open		Shorted	
Stop Input	Open		Shorted	
Contactor A N/O	Open		Shorted	
Contactor B N/O	Open		Shorted	
Local Isolator N/O	Open		Shorted	
Interlock 1	Open		Shorted	
Interlock 2	Open		Shorted	
Interlock 3	Open		Shorted	
Interlock 4	Open		Shorted	
Interlock 5	Open		Shorted	
Interlock 6	Open		Shorted	
Interlock 7	Open		Shorted	
Interlock 8	Open		Shorted	
Interlock 9	Open		Shorted	
Interlock 10	Open		Shorted	

GE Multilin Training Course Selector

Having personnel well trained on the digital relays they are responsible for is an essential element in maximizing the useful life of a relay. By understanding the ins and outs of a relays features and capabilities, personnel will more quickly identify problems, will properly react to situations, and be able to maximize the useful information captured by the devices.

Not all people working with relays require the same training. For example, the needs of relay maintenance personnel will differ from the needs of a power system consultant. The courses listed on the following pages outline the types of training courses offered by GE Multilin Advanced Training Services. Broken down by course type (Theoretical, Product Application, and System Integration), each course is further identified with suggestions for the type of personnel who would benefit most from taking the course. Courses appropriate for Maintenance and Electrical Personnel are identified in this way.

For more information on GE Multilin Advanced Training Services, visit:
www.GEDigitalEnergy.com/training

Theoretical Courses	Catalog Number	Maintenance & Electrical Personnel	Protection Engineers	HMI & System Integrators	Power System Consultants
Fundamentals of Modern Protective Relaying	TRNG-FMPR	x			x
Power System Protection for Industrial Facilities	TRNG-PIND	x			
Power System Protection for Utilities	TRNG-PUTL	x			
Industrial Power System Communications	TRNG-ICOM	x	x	x	x
Utility Power System Communications	TRNG-UCOM		x	x	x
Introduction to the IEC 61850 Protocol	TRNG-61850		x	x	x
Fundamentals of Arc Flash Safety	TRNG-ARCF	x	x		x
Fault Investigation & Analysis	TRNG-FAULT	x	x		x
Introduction to Electromechanical Relays	TRNG-EMR1	x	x		
Product Application Courses					
Metering					
Metering with the PQM and EPM series Meters	TRNG-METER	x		x	x
Distribution					
Distribution Protection (SR745, SR750/760)	TRNG-DIST	x			
SR745 Transformer Management Relay	TRNG-745		x		x
SR750/760 Feeder Management Relay	TRNG-750/760		x		x
F60/F35 Feeder Management Relay	TRNG-F60		x		x
T35/T60 Transformer Management Relay	TRNG-T60		x		x
B30/B90 Bus Protection Relay	TRNG-B30		x		x
F650 Bay Controller	TRNG-F650	x	x	x	x
DDS Distribution Protection	TRNG-DDS		x		x
Motor					
Motor Protection (MM300, 239, 269 Plus, 369, SR469, SPM, M60)	TRNG-MOTR	x			
MM300 Motor Management Relay	TRNG-MM300		x		x
239 Motor Management Relay	TRNG-239		x		x
269 Plus Motor Management Relay	TRNG-269		x		x
369 Motor Management Relay	TRNG-369		x		x
SR469 Motor Management Relay	TRNG-469		x		x
SPM Synchronous Motor Protection Relay	TRNG-SPM		x		x
M60 Motor Management Relay	TRNG-M60		x		x
Generator					
Generator Protection (SR489, DGP, G60)	TRNG-GEN	x			
SR489 Generator Management Relay	TRNG-489		x		x
G60 Generator Management Relay	TRNG-G60		x		x
DGP Generator Protection Relay	TRNG-DGP		x		x

www.GEMultilin.com/training

Product Application Courses (cont'd)	Catalog Number	Maintenance & Electrical Personnel	Protection Engineers	HMI & System Integrators	Power System Consultants
Transmission					
Transmission Line Protection (ALPS, D60, L90, L60)	TRNG-LINE	×			
L90 Line Current Differential Relays/L60 Phase Comparison	TRNG-L90		×		×
D30/D60 Line Distance Relay	TRNG-D60		×		×
D90Plus Line Distance Relay	TRNG-D90		×		×
ALPS/LPS Line Distance Relay	TRNG-ALPS		×		×
Universal Relay					
UR Maintenance	TRNG-URMA	×			
UR Platform	TRNG-URPL		×	×	×
UR Data Communications	TRNG-URDC		×	×	×
UR Advanced Applications	TRNG-URAPPS		×		×
Lentronics Multiplexers					
JungleMux SONET Multiplexer Product Overview Training	TRNG-JMUX1				×
JungleMux SONET Multiplexer Hands-On Training	TRNG-JMUX2			×	
TN1U/TN1Ue SDH Multiplexer	TRNG-TN1U			×	
System Integration Courses					
Substation Automation Fundamentals	TRNG-SAUTO		×		×
Power Management Control Systems Integrator Training	TRNG-PMCS			×	×
EnerVista™ Software Suite Integration	TRNG-EV	×	×	×	×
Interactive Learning CDs					
Fundamentals of Modern Protective Relaying	TRCD-FMPR-C-S-1	×		×	×
Industrial Power System Communications	TRCD-ICOM-C-S-1	×	×	×	×
Utility Power System Communications	TRCD-UCOM-C-S-1		×	×	×
IEC 61850	TRCD-61850-CS1		×	×	×
UR Applications I	TRCD-URA1-C-S-1	×	×	×	×
Distance Protection with the D60 Relay	TRCD-D60-C-S-1	×	×		×
Feeder Protection with the F60/F35	TRCD-F60-C-S-1	×	×		×
Feeder Protection with the SR750/SR760	TRCD-SR750-C-S-1	×	×		×
Feeder Protection with the F650	TRCD-F650-C-S-1	×	×		×
Motor Protection with the SR469	TRCD-M469-C-S-1	×	×		×
Motor Protection with the 369	TRCD-M369-C-S-1	×	×		×
Motor Protection with the 269 Plus	TRCD-M269-C-S-1	×	×		×
Transformer Protection with the SR745	TRCD-SR745-C-S-1	×	×		×
Generator Protection with the SR489	TRCD-SR489-C-S-1	×	×		×
GE Multilin Product Maintenance	TRCD-PRMAINT-C-S-1	×	×		

EnerVista™ Quick Tips

EnerVista™ Quick Tips are useful application notes that aid users in getting the most out of their EnerVista™ software programs. The following Quick Tips apply to the recommended practices for use and maintenance of digital relays that were discussed in this Handbook. The Quick Tips cover topics such as the automatic retrieval of relay information, the creation of a monitoring system, methods for ensuring setting file integrity, and ways to improve relay security.

The software programs featured in the following EnerVista™ Quick Tips are:

EnerVista™ Viewpoint Maintenance

A must-have tool for any integrators or electrical staff involved in power system protection and maintenance. This software package increases the security of relays, reports device operating status, and simplifies device troubleshooting.

EnerVista™ Viewpoint Monitoring

A powerful, yet simple to use, monitoring and data recording software application for small systems that provides total visibility and control of power systems and substations. By communicating with intelligent electronic devices, Viewpoint Monitoring provides an overall view of the entire power system, as well as collecting critical real-time and historical disturbance data to assist with analyzing power system events.

EnerVista™ Launchpad

A powerful toolset management engine for the support resources needed for GE Multilin products, including setup software, manuals, and firmware files. The Launchpad subscription mechanism ensures that necessary files are kept up-to-date and that only updates of interest are send. The EnerVista™ Setup tools provide a consistent look-and-feel for GE Multilin devices, shortening learning curves and increasing productivity.

EnerVista™ Quick Tip 1:

Reduce the Time Required to Retrieve Fault Information from your Devices

When a system fault occurs, the first step in troubleshooting is to retrieve all of the available critical fault information from the devices protecting the system. Depending on the location of the protection relays, and the number of devices that need to be accessed, simply retrieving the required troubleshooting information can cause additional and expensive down time.

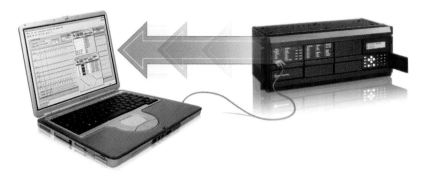

The Viewpoint Monitoring software package provides automatic retrieval of Event Records and Oscillography files from all connected GE Multilin devices. Automatically retrieving the critical fault data means that as soon as the fault occurs, you will have all of the information needed for troubleshooting at your fingertips.

VIEWPOINT monitoring

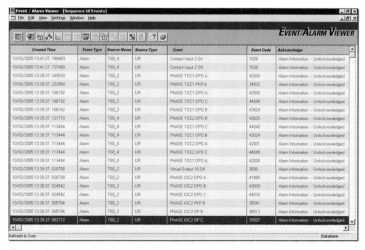

Figure 1
System Event Record

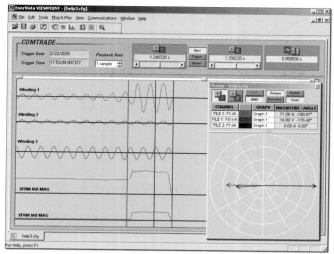

Figure 2
Automatically Retrieved Oscillography File

The following steps will outline how to configure Viewpoint Monitoring to automatically download Events & Waveforms.

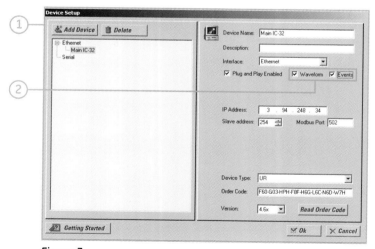

Figure 3

① Click on *Device Setup* from the *Viewpoint Monitoring* main page to launch the Setup window.

② After entering all of the required communications settings, make sure that the *Waveform* and *Events* boxes have been checked.

As soon as the device configuration is complete, Viewpoint Monitoring will connect to the relay and download all event and waveform files. As new event and waveform files are generated by the relay, they will be automatically downloaded to Viewpoint Monitoring.

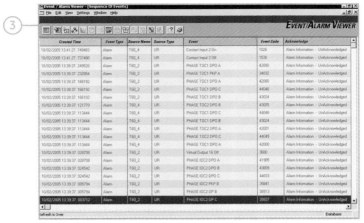

Figure 4

③ To view the saved Events, select the *Events* option from *Viewpoint Monitoring*. The *Event/Alarm Viewer* window will open, allowing you to view all of the events that have been recorded from all devices connected to the *Viewpoint Monitoring* software.

This information can be sorted based on a number of criteria, including the device it originated from, when the event occurred, as well as the cause of the event.

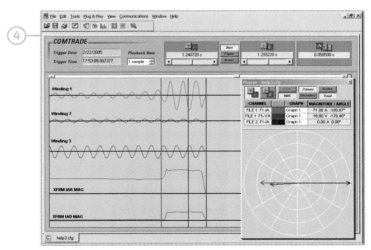

Figure 5

④ To view the saved Waveform files, select *Waveforms* from the Viewpoint Monitoring main page. Select *View* from the *Automated Retrieval* window.

When a file is selected, the comtrade viewer will open, displaying the selected waveforms.

To download a no charge 15 day trial of Viewpoint Monitoring

visit www.GEDigitalEnergy.com/Multilin/EnerVista

EnerVista™ Quick Tip 2:

Never Load Protection Settings into the Wrong Relay Again

GE Multilin has devised a method to safeguard users from erroneously sending protection settings to the wrong relay. This method, called Serial Number Locking is built into the EnerVista™ Setup Program that comes with GE Multilin relays.

Serial Number Locking gives users the ability to "lock" a setting file to a specific device by associating the setting file with the unique serial number of the relay. Once the setting file is "locked" to that relay's serial number, it cannot be sent to any other relay. This feature offers users the security of knowing that the proper settings are being loaded into the proper relay.

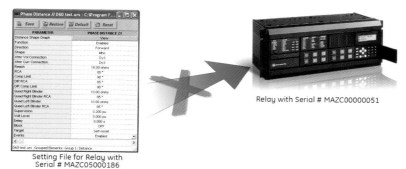

Setting File for Relay with
Serial # MAZC05000186

Relay with Serial # MAZC00000051

EnerVista™ Setup programs verify that the serial number that the setting file was created for, matches the serial number found in the relay

Here's an example of how it works:

1. Using the EnerVista™ Setup program for the GE Multilin product you are configuring, click on the setting file in the OFF-LINE window that you wish to assign a Serial Number to.

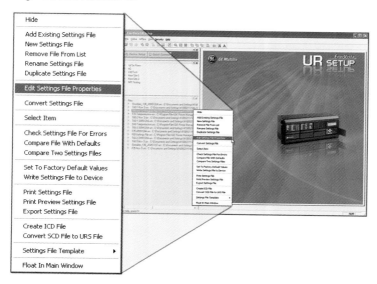

2. Right Click your mouse and select Edit Setting File Properties from the pop-up window.

3. In the window that appears, enter the Serial Number of the relay that this setting file is intended for in the field labeled Serial # Lock.

4. Click on the OK button. This setting file has now been "locked" to that relay.

When a file that has a Serial Number Lock enabled is sent to a relay, the file will only be loaded into the relay if the two serial numbers match. If the two serial numbers do not match, loading of these settings will not be permitted.

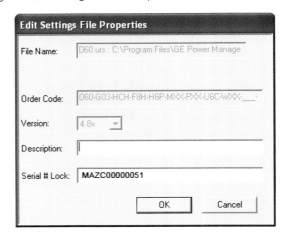

Tip: The serial number of the relay can be found on the label on the rear of the relay or by using the keypad on the front of the relay, located under Actual Values, Product Information.

EnerVista™ Quick Tip 3:

Ensure all Critical Fault Data is Always Retrieved

When a fault occurs in your power system, there is some key information that quickly needs to be retrieved to help determine the cause. Viewpoint Maintenance will allow the user to gather and archive all of this critical information with a Single-Click of the mouse. The information that will be collected by Viewpoint Maintenance includes:

- Relay Type
- Relay Order Code
- Relay Firmware Version

- Setting File
- Oscillography or waveform captures

- Event Record
- Fault Reports
- Data Logger

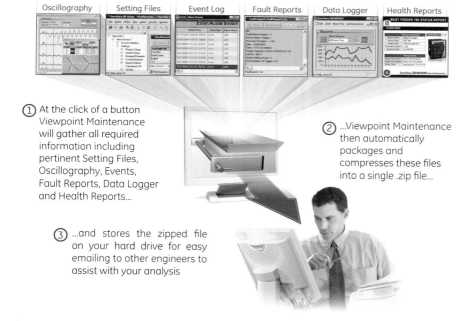

① At the click of a button Viewpoint Maintenance will gather all required information including pertinent Setting Files, Oscillography, Events, Fault Reports, Data Logger and Health Reports...

② ...Viewpoint Maintenance then automatically packages and compresses these files into a single .zip file...

③ ...and stores the zipped file on your hard drive for easy emailing to other engineers to assist with your analysis

The following procedure will demonstrate how to easily collect all critical fault information:

1. Plug your computer into the serial port found on the front of your relay, or connect your computer to the same Local Area Network (LAN) as your relay.

2. On the Viewpoint Maintenance main page, click on the menu item labeled Fault Diagnostic. See Figure 1.

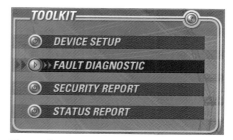

Figure 1
Viewpoint Maintenance main page

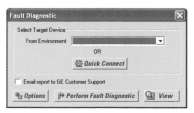

Figure 2

Figure 3

3. Press the Quick Connect button and enter the communications information to match that of the relay you need to diagnose. Press the connect button. See Figure 2 and Figure 3

4. Press the Perform Fault Diagnostic button.

Viewpoint Maintenance will systematically retrieve and archive all of the information listed on the previous page and then allow you to view all of this information on the included fault analysis viewers. See Figure 4.

Figure 4 *The information retrieved by Viewpoint Maintenance includes a report that indicates the current status of your relay and protected equipment.*

(1) **Ensure all Critical Fault Data is Always Retrieved**

(2) **Description of the GE Multilin Relay and equipment being protected**

- Equipment Name
- Relay Model Number and Firmware version
- Relay serial Number
- Intelligent Reporting raises red flags to draw attention to disabled protection or control elements

(3) **Equipment Targets and Alarms detected by the relay**

- Motor Overload
- Hot RTD Alarm
- Loss of Load

(4) **Current Operating Condition of the equipment**

- Motor Speed
- Transformer Load
- Tap Changer Position
- Estimated Time to Trip

(5) **Critical information that can aid in anticipating faults**

- Differential Currents
- Temperature
- Frequency

(6) **Historical Information about the asset that aids in predicting maintenance requirements**

- Motor Running hours
- Accumulated Loss of Life
- Number of Breaker Operations

The Viewpoint Maintenance software package provides several other easy to use reports that help you determine the current or historical operating conditions of your devices. The Settings Audit Trail report shown in Figure 5 provides you with information about setting changes that have been made to your relays. The information found in this report includes when setting changes have been made, who changed them, and what changes were made at that time.

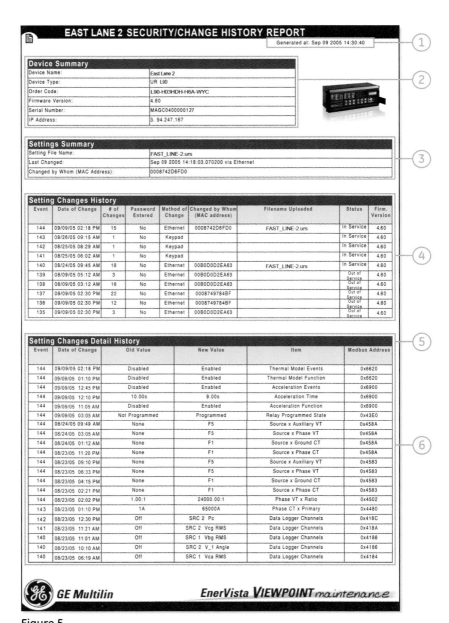

Figure 5

Easily track any configuration changes that have been made to you relays.

(1) **Date and Time that the Security Report was generated**

(2) **Description of the GE Multilin Relay**
- Equipment Name
- Relay Model Number and Firmware version
- Relay Serial Number

(3) **Summary of the last time the configuration was changed**
- Name of setting file
- Who loaded the file
- When the file was loaded

(4) **History of last 10 occurrences the configuration was changed**
- Date and time of configuration change
- Number of settings changed at this time
- Method used to change the relay settings
- MAC address of computer sending settings
- Name of the setting file sent to the Relay
- The relay status after the settings changes

(5) **Detailed description of all changes made to the relay's configuration**
- Date and time of configuration change
- Description of the setting that was changed
- Setting value before change was made
- Setting value after change was made

(6) **Convenient File Format**
- On-line and off-line copies
- Easily zip these reports with other pertinent files such as setting files and fault reports to share with engineers

To download a no charge 15 day trial of Viewpoint Maintenance
visit www.GEDigitalEnergy.com/Multilin/EnerVista

EnerVista™ Quick Tip 4:

Ensure Relay Settings Match Those Programmed In The Settings File

Incorrectly programmed protection devices create a serious security risk to the stability and reliability of your protection system. Periodically confirming that the device settings are programmed the same as the original settings issued by the protection engineer ensures that the relay's operation will match the system specifications.

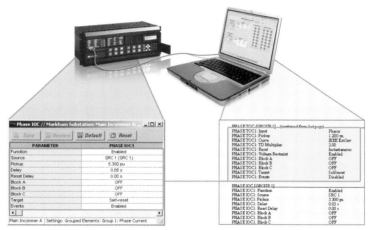

Figure 1
Identify the differences between the Setting File and the Relay's configuration

GE Multilin's *EnerVista™ UR Setup* program allows you to compare the settings that are programmed in a relay with a file stored on your computer. This can be done while the relay is online and protecting the system, requiring no down time at all. When completed, a report will be generated outlining any settings in the relay which do not match the settings programmed in the file.

The following is an example of how to compare the relay settings to a saved file.

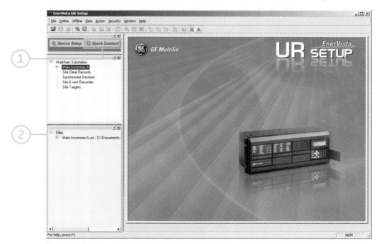

Figure 2

(1) Select the *Quick Connect* button and enter the information required to establish communications with your relay.

(2) Right click in the *Offline Window* and select *Add Existing Settings File.* Open the saved file associated with your relay.

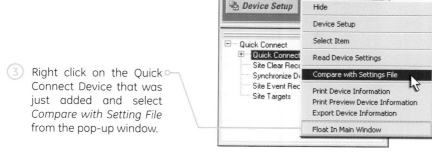

(3) Right click on the Quick Connect Device that was just added and select *Compare with Setting File* from the pop-up window.

Figure 3

(4) A window will open asking you to select which file you wish to use for the comparison. Any files that have been opened in the *UR Setup* program's Offline Window will appear here.

Select your file, and then OK.

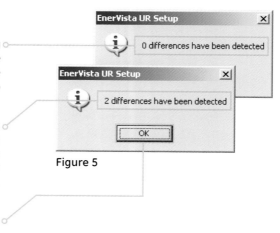

Figure 4

If the relay's programming matches all settings in the saved file, a message will be displayed indicating that no differences were found.

If the relay's programming does not match the settings in the saved file, a message will be displayed indicating the number of settings that are not the same.

Selecting OK will generate a report of all mismatched settings.

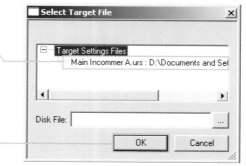

Figure 5

Setting Difference Example

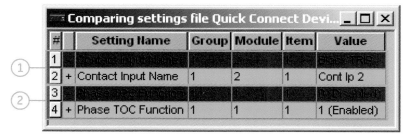

Figure 6

① *Example 1:* Relay settings have Contact Input 2 named as *Block TRIP*. The settings file has the contact named *Cont Ip 2*.

② *Example 2:* Relay settings has the Phase Time Overcurrent (TOC) *Disabled*. The settings file has the TOC function *Enabled*.

EnerVista™ Quick Tip 5:

Enhance System Security while Providing Traceability to Device Settings

In today's utility and industrial applications, system security has become one of the greatest challenges. Part of this challenge is ensuring that the settings programmed into system devices are not changed, either by accident, or intentionally. Any change in the protection configuration can jeopardize system reliability and functionality.

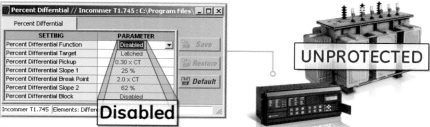

Figure 1
*A simple settings change to disable a protective element
can leave system equipment unprotected.*

The *Viewpoint Maintenance* software package provides an easy to use Security Audit Trail. This report will outline when a device's settings were changed, who made the changes, as well as the specific settings and values which have been altered.

VIEWPOINT maintenance

① **Date and Time that the Security Report was generated**

② **Description of the GE Multilin Relay**
- Equipment Name
- Relay Model Number and Firmware version
- Relay Serial Number

③ **Summary of the last time the configuration was changed**
- Name of setting file
- Who loaded the file
- When the file was loaded

④ **History of last 10 occurrences the configuration was changed**
- Date and time of configuration change
- Number of settings changed at this time
- Method used to change the relay settings
- MAC address of computer sending settings
- Name of the setting file sent to the Relay
- The relay status after the settings changes

(5) **Detailed description of all changes made to the relay's configuration**

- Date and time of configuration change
- Description of the setting that was changed
- Setting value before change was made
- Setting value after change was made

(6) **Convenient File Format**

- On-line and off-line copies
- Easily zip these reports with other pertinent files such as setting files and fault reports to share with engineers

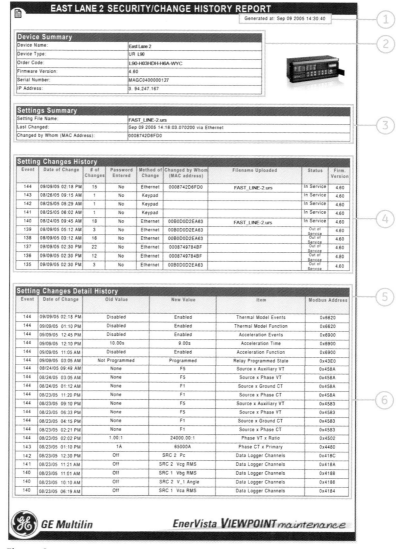

Figure 2

To create your Security Audit Report, simply perform the following steps:

1. Open Viewpoint Maintenance and select Security Report.

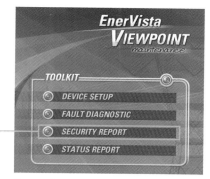

Figure 3

2. Select the device you wish to create the Security Report for.

   Note: If the device is not seen in the drop down menu, it will need to be configured under the Device Setup menu of Viewpoint Maintenance.

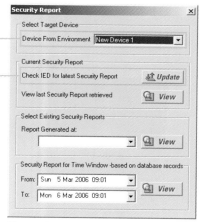

Figure 4

3. Select the Check IED for latest Security Report button to perform the settings verification.

   Note: When performing security reports for relays that do not store the Security Audit Trail internally a security report will not be generated the first time the program is run. The settings will be saved from the relay, and these settings will be used as the baseline for any future reports.

4. To view Security Reports that were previously generated, select the date that the report was created from the Select Existing Security Reports drop down menu.

Figure 5

To download a no charge 15 day trial of Viewpoint Maintenance visit www.GEDigitalEnergy.com/Multilin/EnerVista

EnerVista™ Quick Tip 6:

Create a Simple Network to Monitor Your Protection and Metering Devices

Creating a communications network to remotely monitor and control your protection and monitoring devices can be done in an easy and cost effective manner. The following procedure will demonstrate how to create a communications network and begin monitoring your devices through an HMI software program.

Connecting your Network

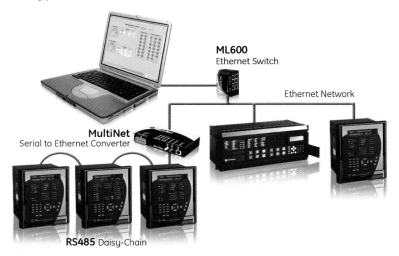

ML600
Ethernet Switch

Ethernet Network

MultiNet
Serial to Ethernet Converter

RS485 Daisy-Chain

Figure 1

1. If your protection or metering device is equipped with an Ethernet port, connect this port to an ML600 unmanaged Ethernet switch using a RJ45 Ethernet cable.

2. Using the keypad on the front panel of your relay or meter, program the device with an IP Address that is unique to that device. (An IP Address is a 4 segment number that is used to uniquely identify an Ethernet device found on a network i.e. 3.94.234.27)

3. Using the keypad on the front panel of your relay or meter, program the device with a Modbus slave address.

4. If your relays and meters do not have an Ethernet port, connect these devices to a MultiNet Serial to Ethernet converter and connect the MultiNet to the ML600 unmanaged Ethernet Switch using a RJ45 Ethernet cable. See Figure 1.

   (To learn how to connect your devices to a MultiNet converter, please see Quick Tip #2)

5. If you are connecting this network to an existing network, plug your ML600 into your LAN using a RJ45 Ethernet cable.

6. If you are not connecting this network to an existing network, plug your computer directly into the ML600 using a RJ45 Ethernet cable. You will then need to assign your computer a Static IP Address. To learn how to do this, see Appendix A at the end of this quick tip.

Monitoring your Devices

To monitor your relays and meters using the Viewpoint Monitoring software program, complete the following steps:

1. Start up the software and click on the Device Setup button to configure the communication settings.

2. Press the Add Device Button.

3. In the filed labeled IP Address, enter the IP Address of the relay or meter that you want to communicate to. If you are communicating to your device using a MultiNet serial to Ethernet converter, enter the IP Address of the MultiNet. See Figure 2.

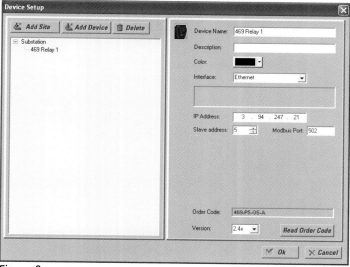

Figure 2

4. In the field labeled Slave Address, enter the Modbus Slave address that is programmed into this GE Multilin device.

5. Press the Read Order Code button.

6. Press the Add Device button and complete the above steps for each additional device you are going to monitor and press OK.

7. Press the Plug and Play – IED Dashboard button found near the top of the screen.

9. Click on the device you wish to monitor and press the Dashboard button found below it. See Figure 3.

10. Begin monitoring your relays and meters to analyze the status of your critical

Figure 3

power system equipment. See Figure 4.

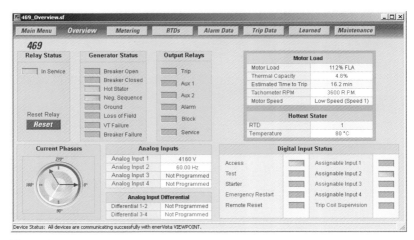

Figure 4
Viewpoint Monitoring will detect the devices you are using and automatically
generate monitoring screens that are tailored to your devices and wiring configurations.

Now that you can communicate with your devices, Viewpoint Monitoring will allow you to easily monitor, control, and analyze historical data about your power system using the following tools.

Single-Line Monitoring

The Single-Line Diagrams allows you to create customized Single-Line Monitoring screens that will display real-time information from multiple devices on one screen and allow for sending commands (i.e. Trip/Close) to these relays and meters. See Figure 5.

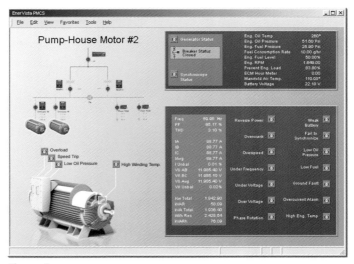

Figure 5
Monitor the status of multiple devices to identify System problems

Annunciator Alarming

The Annunciator Alarm screens will monitor any measured parameter and generate alarms whenever a digital value changes state (i.e. Breaker Status) or an analog value drifts beyond a preset value (i.e. Transformer Load). See Figure 6.

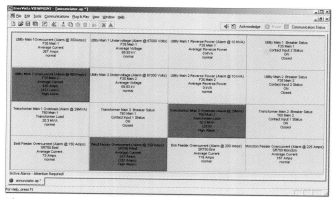

Figure 6
Get Instant Notification of System Alarms from any device on your Network

Trending Reports

The Trending Reports allow you to log measured parameters over long periods of time and provides a method for analyzing these values for changes over any time period. See Figure 7.

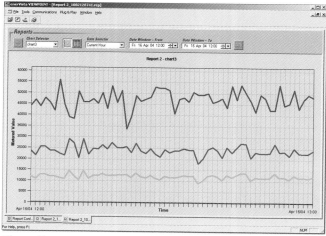

Figure 7
Log Power Level data from multiple devices at one time

Assign your computer a "Static IP Address" that will allow your computer to communicate on your new network by performing the following steps.

1. Open your computers control panel by clicking on your Start Menu > Settings > Control Panel icon.

2. Double click on the icon labeled Network Connections.

3. Right Click your mouse on the icon labeled Local Area Connection and select Properties.

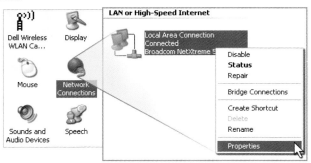

4. In the menu that appears, select the item labeled Internet Protocol (TCP/IP) and then click on the Properties button.

5. Select the tab labeled Use the following IP address.

6. Enter an IP Address, a Subnet Mask, and a Default Gateway address in their respective fields and press OK.

Tip:
The IP address for your computer must be a unique address found on this network. The subnet mask must be the same for all devices or computers found on this network. If you are unsure what number to use here, select 255.255.0.0 or contact your network administrator.

To download a no charge 15 day trial of Viewpoint Monitoring

visit www.GEDigitalEnergy.com/Multilin/EnerVista